# SHADOWS

They grew up in small towns and big cities. They found out about sex in alleys, train stations, and at frat parties. Dated debs, Southern belles, and boys next door. They discovered love and learned how to hide it.

They suffered quack psychiatry, were blacklisted as undesirables, and sent lovers off to war with a handshake. Through four decades of dangerous times, and changing times, through depression, war, McCarthy and Kinsey, they lived their lives in hiding.

But they coped, and they were successful. Because, more than just friends, the four of them were family.

# A History of Shadows

## ROBERT C. REINHART

**AVON**
PUBLISHERS OF BARD, CAMELOT, DISCUS AND FLARE BOOKS

A HISTORY OF SHADOWS is an original publication
of Avon Books. This work has never before appeared in
book form.


AVON BOOKS
A division of
The Hearst Corporation
959 Eighth Avenue
New York, New York 10019

First Avon Printing, April, 1982

For Jean B., Charles R., and
those I've met through Bill W.

# Dedication

This book is a quartet of voices, sometimes harmonious, sometimes dissonant. Three of the voices you'll hear in these pages are still living, one is now dead. It is the now silent voice that sustained the "melody line" when the pitch of the others was off. It is to the perfect pitch of Wesley Ober that I owe the greatest debt.

This book is dedicated to that quartet:

The late Wesley Ober, a voice from a lost stage;
Robert Regal, a voice of rectitude;
Carl Mason, a musical voice;
Billy Hicks, a voice for grace notes.

The voices are real, though the names are fictional. As well, some of the facts of the quartet's lives have been altered to protect their privacy. As one of them said to me, "My secret is the habit of a lifetime. I've needed my secret so long that I can't imagine being without it. I'm too old to be nakedly gay."

CHARLES NORMAN
*April 10, 1981*

# Preface

This book is about the lives of four gay men. Three are in their sixties, one is in his seventies. This book is a chronicle of their lives as gay people, and of the "family" they have been to one another for over four decades.

The idea for this book came from a simple observation made by a friend as we passed the site of the long-closed Stonewall Bar.

For those who may not know about the Stonewall, it was the site of the June 1969 riot by gays against the police who had come to raid the bar. For the first time, instead of acknowledging the right of the police to take any action they wanted against gays, the gay men in the bar resisted arrest and rioted, driving off the police. Their precedent-setting protest was profound in that they asserted that gays have the right to assemble, and it was a right that they were finally going to claim. The Stonewall Riot was the first overt action by gays in what was to become an ongoing fight for their civil rights. Stonewall was a milestone.

But on that day when my friend and I passed where the Stonewall had been, he said, "It's gone and you'd never know it had been there. What a shame. It was so important." His comment set off the chain of thought and event that led to this book.

I won't attempt to trace in detail the thought processes by which I determined to write a gay oral history, because my thoughts led me through labyrinths of politics, history, and society's ongoing need to suppress minorities. Other books deal with these matters. These books do so fully, and it was never my intention to produce an exhaustive chronicle.

I was and am deeply disturbed by the suppression that has kept gay people divided—remote from one another—and limited in their visions of their futures, and almost completely devoid of a past as a minority.

However, my decision to undertake work on a gay history had one grave defect: I didn't know where to begin. What history? Where? Who? To what purpose?

Like the basic idea of this book, its focus came from a casual remark. I was at a dinner party where a man in his mid-sixties said, "You young people have it made. When I was your age we were all in hiding. We hung together, but we hid."

When he was my age? That would have been in the 1930s. I realized that he was talking of a lost age, or an age almost lost.

I began to wonder what it was like to be gay in that decade, and then I began to wonder about the decades closer in time to mine. What was it like to be gay then? Was it different? How did it affect gay people? How did a gay person in the thirties decide on a career, live with a lover, find sex, cope with oppression, attain self-esteem, make friends, hide gayness or reveal it to his family?

I decided to find out. What I found is in these pages.

Initially, I wanted to write this book for my doctoral dissertation, but was informed by my counselor and others at my school that the subject would not be well received and could adversely affect my employability after I left school.

I learned that I had more in common with the past than I had imagined.

My first plan was to write a general history of gay life in the decades from the thirties on, but the available material, mostly from the heterosexual press or the psychiatric journals of those years, was airless and bloodless, when it wasn't despising or demeaning.

As an historian I believed that no era is an abstract thing: It is a lived experience, a drama played within the moods and forces at work in the world at that time.

So I sought help and after much inquiry found the four men from whose experience I culled this book. I chose these four because all had known one another since the early thirties and had in a very real sense become a family, by turns loving, irritated, critical, supportive, and caring. But always together, always near one another.

I interviewed each alone, starting with a questionnaire and pursuing the line of questioning based on my growing understanding of what they revealed.

If the reader notes a strong emphasis on the sexual lives of these men, it is because that is exactly what I tried to elicit in the interviews. Also, I sought those events in their lives when, because of their homosexuality, they made choices, took turnings, or feared to do something lest they reveal their homosexuality.

Also, because memory is not always orderly and chronological, I have reordered conversations so that, as nearly as possible, each story is narrated chronologically. I have taken only those liberties with the subject's way of speaking that clarity demanded.

Hundreds of hours of taped interviews were sifted into these four parallel—often commingled—stories which in a way, I feel add up to *one* history of a time.

Even now, I'm not sure the book "reveals" anything, "proves" anything, but it is a slice of the gay past as seen by four men who lived "gay" in New York over the past four decades.

# PART 1

## Tuning Up

# Carl Mason

I'm not sure I should be talking to you. How discreet are you? Well, we can start anyway.

If you've read that dreary little biography that silly man wrote about me, you know most of the facts. He did get the facts straight. Well, most of them anyway.

I was at Warners from 1936 till after World War II. That was over thirty years.

I free-lanced after that, a score here, a score there. Just like the old dames, I even did two horror movies. Great fun.

Now, suddenly, my scores are legitimate. I was camp in the sixties. Next year, the Pittsburgh Symphony and San Francisco Symphony will perform programs of my compositions. Nonesuch Records is talking of doing a complete library of my works. My God, even the theme music from *Undaunted* is a disco hit.

No, young man, I don't think it's "belated recognition of great talent." I've just lasted longer than any of the others. Like old Bette, I'm durable. Sometimes very good, sometimes awful, but always durable . . . and never boring.

Just what is it you really want to know?

Oh, do cut the historian's jargon. If you want to know with whom I slept and what we did when, forget it. Sex was always secondary for me. I had a great career at a very exciting time . . . in a very exciting place.

No, I kept my sex life secret. I couldn't have survived at the studio otherwise. Imagine Jack Warner harboring a known fag. Not in that business, not then. Not even now, I would guess. You know how people are.

The favorite phrase for my work was "soaring melodic line." If they'd known I was gay they would have called my work "pleasant enough, but lightweight." That's the way of the

3

world. If I'd admitted I was gay, I would have trivialized myself. Yes, you could say self-respect kept me in the closet . . . if you feel you must.

Well, since I don't care to talk of sex, then what?

Just being gay?

Well, I didn't exactly hide it, but I certainly didn't flaunt it. Let me think.

# Billy Hicks

I'm sorry, but we're going to have less time than I told you. Some sofas are arriving a day early from the upholsterer and Mrs. F. gets very upset if I'm not there to hold her hand and personally tend to things.

We don't call them customers, darling, we call them clients. And I'm not a decorator, I'm a designer.

My clients? They're the kind you never see in the pages of magazines like *House & Garden*. Frankly, that kind of publicity is considered a little vulgar by my clients. Besides, I don't "decorate" their homes: I take the pieces they want to use— Grandmother's *escritoire,* Great-Grandfather's silver—and arrange a comfortable setting. And not for the camera to look at, but for people to live in.

I started as an architect, but . . . well, something happened. It's not important.

There's not time to go into that.

Just what is it you have in mind?

Being gay? Is that all? What's there to say about it? I had a lover for twenty years. He died. We lived quietly. The way most married people do, I suppose. Nothing very exciting in that.

His name was Teddy. Teddy Downs. He was a lovely boy. He was my baby.

Look, I'm sorry, darling, but I have to leave. You can come back if you want, but I don't think I've much to tell you.

# Robert Regal

Machines make me nervous. Can't you just take notes?

I know it doesn't make any noise, but I can see the reels moving. Yes, put it out of sight. Thank you.

I should warn you that I'm not a very good talker. My business is figures, accounts. Do you know anything about accounting? Then you know we deal only in the verifiable.

You said you wouldn't use my name. Have you picked a—what do you call it?—yes, a pseudonym.

Robert Regal? Sounds like a movie star. And that's the way you'll label your tapes. You're sure. I guess it's all right, then.

The others are much better talkers than I am. . . . Talk the ears off a brass monkey. Me, I'm facts and figures.

Of course I've talked about being gay. If you are, you talk about it. But this is different. This is so formal. And it will be published.

Yes, I'm a little afraid. . . . I'm in my sixties and I've gotten this far without any trouble, and I don't want any.

I suppose some people guess I am, but what they don't know . . . I've been very careful.

No, a lover never seemed to fit. You know what business I'm in. If there'd been the slightest breath of scandal . . .

I don't know why Billy mentioned that. I'll give him hell. That was a long time ago and it's nobody's business. It's well past and well forgotten.

Maybe some other time. No, there's no reason to go into that

I'll answer your questions. If it weren't for the others I'd have never agreed. What good will it do?

No, I don't feel oppressed.

Yes, I wish I were different. I'm not.

# Wesley Ober

You mean that little machine can hear me if I just whisper? Remarkable.

You know, I don't care whether you use my real name or not. I'm seventy-one. Who the hell would care whether I'm a cocksucker or not? But I suppose the others are right. If you use my real name, there are a lot of people who could connect what I say to them.

Let's talk about sex. Do you want real names? Could you use them without getting sued? You couldn't. What a pity. Most people love a little good gossip.

Well, I haven't been on a stage in eight years. I was never all that great, but I got by, and it was a wonderful life.

I still see a lot of the old crowd. So many are gone. I'm a survivor. My God, child, I was in *Intolerance*. I was an angel, an avenging angel, in that movie. I had a good body. There were five—no, six—angels, and we were wired to fly. It was a night shot and Griffith wanted us to wing down over the fleeing sinners brandishing swords. We'd take off from a high platform, but there was always one of us who couldn't hold the pose. He'd go limp, so they'd land us and we'd trudge back to the takeoff place, get rewired, and off we'd go again. It was supposed to be one night's work, but it took three nights to get the shot. We were all kids and we were getting seventeen-fifty a night. A lot for a kid in those days.

I was a hick from a large Southern family, but I got along with people. I was liked and welcome. I liked to have fun and could tell a good story.

I've been thinking about this interview and trying to figure out why anyone would be interested in what four old farts had to say about being gay.

9

Sure it had an effect on the way we lived. You bet your ass.

But I was luckier than most. I could fuck anything. I preferred men, but I could get it up for boys, starlets, or roosters. What's the difference? Saved my ass many times.

I remember once at MGM when ＿＿＿＿＿ was at her height. A big star. A German guy I'd met in New York came out to test. He had everything going for him and the test was terrific. But one night he had to squire ＿＿＿＿＿ to an opening, and when he took her home he was too courtly and European to just go in and lay the cunt. He saw her to her door. Now, there was no one who didn't screw her or at least make a pass. It was a point of honor with her. Her feelings were hurt, so she got on the phone and called Louis B. Mayer to tell him that this new guy he was testing was a fag. That nipped *that* career in the bud.

Sure, being gay meant something then. It still does, and what it means isn't very good. I was careful. I was quiet about it. I'd have been crazy not to be. But you poke a lady now and then, and the word gets around. Just enough. I never overdid it. I never got married.

Regrets? Yes, some.

Why shouldn't I tell you anything you want to know?

I'll tell you. Why don't we do an hour every two or three days. I love to talk, but my doctor clamps down on me. And this is a little tiring for me.

I'll make some notes before we meet again.

I can remember the past better than I can what happened yesterday.

Can you come back Thursday? Good.

Remind me to tell you about the Twentieth star—the guy who Petty used for his women's legs.

All right, remind me to tell you who Petty was.

## PART 2

---

# Opening Theme
## "When You Were Sweet Sixteen"*

*James Thornton's durable vaudeville hit of
the twenties.

# Carl Mason

The studio press release on me said that I was trained in Vienna, "the rhythms of that capital of melody flowing through my veins." I didn't see Vienna till after I left Warners, despite what I told that person who wrote my biography. Vienna's a listless city with wall-to-wall Wiener schnitzel.

I grew up sissy in Chicago. I have a picture of me from then. Let me show you.

See? I'm Buster Brown—big floppy silk tie, velvet suit, and turd curls.

And that's the way my mother would send me up to my piano lessons. She'd get me all dressed up like that and say, "My, but you're a pretty little boy." That absurd-looking infant would have to trudge up to the trolley stop clutching his music bag. Talk about catcalls. That walk was my weekly climb up Calvary.

My mother would fuss at me like a little girl with a doll, but she never held me. She never kissed me. Nor did my father. He was a glum man who always addressed me as "young man."

But I was a prodigy. Almost all people who make major musical careers are. We start young. I was three. I was seven when that picture was taken, and highly proficient. I'd already had three years of lessons by the time I was seven.

The only thing that made that endless walk endurable was my love for that music.

That awful walk. That awful little boy who always waited for me and chanted, "Curly, Curly . . . ain't she a pretty girlie," over and over.

The year after that picture was taken—I was seven, remember—I'd gotten off the trolley near my home and a man got off with me. He's the one who led me down the alley and . . .

13

I don't want to make this sound awful, because I loved it. How can I explain it?

As I said, he got off the trolley behind me and soon he was walking next to me, and he said, "It's dark. Why don't you take my hand?" It was a smooth voice. It didn't offend my musical ear the way neighbors' voices would. That awful accent of my neighborhood. Anyway, he said, "Why don't you come with me and I'll buy you something." There's music to a child's ears. I went with him and he bought me a magazine. I remember that it was a *Saturday Evening Post*. It was like a mark of adulthood to have a big people's magazine, and I cherished it. We walked on, and I didn't feel any fear when he led me into an alley and began to stroke me. It made me feel warm and good . . . loved, I guess.

Then he took his cock out and said I could touch it if I wanted. What an absurd image. Those tiny hands of mine petting his cock as if it were some exotic animal. And then I laid my cheek on it for a while. I remember how hot it felt, how comforting.

Finally he turned away from me and I saw his elbow bobbing and he sighed. I didn't know it then, but I know now that he masturbated.

When he turned back to me he said, "You run along now. You're sure you know your way? Fine. Say you found a nickel. Say that's how you got the magazine."

"I will," I said, and walked home.

That's when I became a seductive child.

I looked for that man on the trolley all the time.

Children know so much. The man on the trolley never came back, but I found that at the movies I could find other men. All I had to do was sit one seat in from the aisle and some man would always come and sit next to me and let me play with him.

Am I making you uneasy? You look it.

I was lucky in one way. My parents never tried to get me to "butch up."

It was Miss Amelson who got me out of the fancy clothes. A lovely, bosomy lady. My fourth-grade teacher. Maybe she was just tired of seeing those dirty tear tracks on my cheeks every time I came in from recess. My mother dressed me for school in a way that clearly said "Hit me" to any other child.

Miss Amelson sent a note home with me, and soon after, she came to visit. When she left, my mother cried for the rest of the day, and I was in despair that I had somehow done something awful to a teacher I loved. That was a Friday.

I'm sure, because the next morning I didn't go to school and my mother took me to a barber and I was shorn of those awful curls. Then she took me to Carson, Pirie and Scott's and bought me knickers, sturdy tweed knickers. And thick wool socks that went up over my thighs. But she wouldn't buy me a cap. She said they were for "toughs."

And Monday when I got to school, Miss Amelson said to me, "My, don't you look the handsome fellow."

Is it any wonder that drag has always made me feel very uneasy?

My father died when I was eight or nine. He didn't seem to leave an empty space. Nothing in our lives changed, except that mother started serving fish occasionally.

What more can I say about my father? Mother never talked about him and I never really knew him.

No one ever said it to me, but I suppose I must have been regarded as a lonely child. I wasn't. Not at all. I had music. My mother's ambition didn't drive me to it and I had no ambition for myself in that area. I just loved music. I loved it no matter where I found it . . . even in the awful piano scores for the silent movies.

And, God, the music was usually awful. Most of the scores were musical rag bags . . . a tatter of Brahms, a frayed bit of Beethoven. And most of the pianists in those smelly old neighborhood movie houses were drunk, often not noticing that the love theme they were playing was underscoring a stampede of cattle or a train being derailed. Sometimes it was very funny. I learned a lot in those theaters. It was unintentional, but I learned by imagining what I would use, if I could provide a score for a movie.

My big dream was to score a William S. Hart movie, because I was mad for him. Him and his sensuous upper lip.

But all my teachers regarded the movies as frivolous. So did I. The reason I went so often was for sex, if a lot of groping about under overcoats can be called sex.

None of my music teachers ever told me that I had learned all I could from them, but I somehow knew, and I moved up the scale of teachers in Chicago until I'd used them up. I sucked up everything they knew.

It never occurred to me to ask where Mother got the money for those expensive lessons. It had always been there, and whenever I told my mother that I wanted to change teachers or undertake a new course, she would simply say, "Fine, dear."

Before I was twenty I had made five guest appearances with the Chicago Symphony. I played the dazzling pieces the young use to show off or to cover their lack of technique. I didn't choose them, the conductors did. I knew better than to just dazzle, even then.

Mother died when I was nineteen. Of course I felt awful, but I was quite capable of taking care of myself. I was quite self-sufficient.

You know, young man, some of the questions you ask imply that I am unfeeling or that I'm blocking out events that I find too traumatic to face. That's nonsense. I hope you're not one of those boring—what do they call them, psychohistorians?—who's going to take everything I say and give it a shellac of psychiatry. I'm telling you what happened to me. No more, no less. It's my life. I don't like the idea that you're going to fiddle with it. I'd hate to have my life reduced to a case study. . . .

Mother died. And that's all. She died. I got an adequate inheritance, got in touch with the best teachers in New York, and left Chicago.

I never missed Chicago, I never went back. I'd made a few friends, none close. For me, the house in which we'd lived was only the place where the piano was. As I found, our money had come from a large amount of Swift's stock. The income was quite good enough for what I wanted. I could afford New York's best teachers.

My last night in Chicago I went to a neighborhood theater. The movies it played were still silent. But the next week, I remember, they were showing *The Jazz Singer*. It was the first sound movie. I can be superstitious and it still strikes me as prophetic that sound movies coincided with my move to New York. *The Jazz Singer* was the first movie I went to see when I got to New York. The first thing I did after checking in at the Y. It was an omen. Most people saw the movie as a novelty. I looked at it and saw the future.

I don't mean anything as dramatic as that may sound. I mean that I saw that movies could never go back to being silent. They were like babies. Once they started talking, you'd never be able to shut them up. And they did babble like babies, for a long time.

And I don't mean that I foresaw the importance of background music. That would come some years later. It was Selznick who pioneered it. However, when his movies showed me what might be done, I saw the point immediately and was very excited.

My eyes weren't on a career when I arrived in New York. I was still learning about my music. I wanted to know all about it. I wanted to have all its secrets. I must have been working seventy hours a week at least, studying composition and arranging and technique and playing. And I had the best teachers in the city.

I made some musician friends at the time, but all we talked about was music. We talked of music the way some men talked of mistresses.

The man who taught me arranging was tops in his field. He worked with . . . But I can't tell you names without giving myself away, can I?

What I was getting to was that the man who taught me arranging was hired by Roxy to do some of the arrangements for the stage shows that accompanied the movies at Roxy's new movie palace over on Seventh Avenue, and he asked me if I'd like to make some money doing some scoring. I said sure. It was a chance to work with the maestro of an actual production. And Roxy's theater, which he'd named after himself, was considered a very exciting, very classy place to work. I loved every minute of the job. I loved being there at 5:30 in the morning for orchestra rehearsals, and I loved the last-minute turmoil of scoring a longer passage to get the dancers off and the next act on. What a wonderful game it was. I'd stay and work, and then I'd often go back in the house and sit and watch the first showing of the movie.

Sometimes Chuck would come and sit with me.

Chuck? He was a chorus boy for Roxy. We eyed one another for a long time at rehearsals. But it was just a lot of sniffing about. But one day we ran into one another at the Rexall Drugstore across from Radio City and we sat and had lunch together.

My God, I was naïve. When I look back on that lunch I realize that Chuck was dropping pins all over the place.

Dropping pins? That means that he was giving me hints that he was gay.

What's the term now? There isn't one? Well, he used words like "butch," and "trade." I thought they were theater terms. The only words I knew were "faggot" and "cocksucker."

I did understand what he was getting at when he gave me his address on a napkin and told me when he was home and when he had a day off. I remember that when he handed me the napkin he put his hand on my shoulder, and when I took the napkin he didn't let go, but kept on talking and ran his hand from my shoulder down to my elbow and slowly massaged my elbow. I had an immediate erection and he looked down, saw it, smiled, and said, "Call."

Naturally, I was in love. He was certainly beautiful.

This is hard for me to believe . . . but Chuck was the first gay man I'd ever spoken to. All the others I'd been with had been "hit and run." We never spoke to one another. Never. I had no idea that homosexuals did anything together but have sex in adjoining theater seats. To mix a metaphor, Chuck turned down a bed and opened a door at the same time.

Sure I remember the first time with Chuck. Who can ever forget the first time. Not that this was the first time I'd ever had sex, but it was the first time in a bed. And when I think of that room, all I can see is that bed that loomed as large as a football field. Acres of bed.

I knew—or I guessed—that straight people had sex on beds, but I never had. And I didn't know gay people went to bed together. I think I expected to find he had two theater seats in his room.

When I went to Chuck's he met me at his door in a robe. I was puffing a little from climbing the five flights to his room over on Forty-seventh, and he opened the door wearing only a robe. I was panicked, and, worst of all, behind him was his bed. I was breathless from the stairs and the sight of the bed made me dizzy. All I could do was stand rooted on his doorstep. He finally had to pull me into the room.

He fell against the door, slamming it, and he reached up and pulled me to him. He kissed me and I remember the panic I felt when he pushed his tongue into my mouth. I didn't know what to do. I was afraid I'd bite it, and there didn't seem to be room enough in there for two tongues.

I think it was then that Chuck fully realized that he had more on his hands than he'd bargained for. What does one do with a virgin? But he was game.

He got out of his robe and helped me out of my coat. You must remember that I'd never touched a naked body, and suddenly there was this very naked man with me, and I didn't know where to start, what to touch first. If he'd been hot as a stove, I couldn't have been more afraid of touching him. He finally had to take my hand and lay it on his thigh. How clear that still is. I can still feel him on the tips of my fingers. He wasn't hot. He felt cool and smooth.

He told me to take my clothes off. I tried, but it seems I'd forgotten how. I did all right with my shirt, but I tried to get my trousers over my shoes and got completely bound up, half in, half out. Then I tried to untie my shoes, up inside my trousers, and knotted the laces.

I was sitting on the edge of the bed, but I didn't dare turn around, because I could feel the bed shaking and I knew Chuck was laughing at me. I felt such a boob.

He got down in front of me and managed to work my trousers off my shoes, unknot them, and get me out of those damned things.

We had sex . . . as best I could. I was so intimidated by our nakedness, and his tongue overwhelmed me.

I was so humorless about the whole thing, so Wagnerian. For Chuck it was all ragtime.

Naturally, I thought that since I'd had sex with Chuck I must be in love with him. And for a long time I was. But I thought I'd made such a fool of myself that he couldn't possibly care to ever see me again. So, I avoided him, I never called.

I ran into Chuck during the war. Which war? The Second *World* War. Yes, that one. He was 4-F and Metro had brought him out to see if they could build him into something. Young actors were scarce. He did fairly well at MGM. We talked about that time I went to his room and he told me that I'd made him feel such an old whore. He told me that he'd found me quite beautiful. He asked me why I'd avoided him, never called again. Funny how things happen.

The week after that thing with Chuck I got a call from Roxy. He said that Paramount needed some help on a Broadway musical they'd bought and were going to shoot at their Long

Island studios. Would I be interested in scoring the show for the soundtrack.

I told him I didn't have any experience with soundtracks and he said, "Who does?" Remember, this is 1931.

I'll tell you the story, but you'll have to disguise it, or you may as well use my real name.

The show they'd bought was a vehicle for a famous comedian. He was a sad-looking little fellow and the story had him in Mexico, where, by an absurd chain of events, he finds himself passing as a famous matador from Spain. Naturally, if he fights the bull and wins, he gets the girl.

The shooting was funnier than the show. Everyone on the movie was stage-trained, except for the camera and sound people. The sets weren't movie sets, they were stage sets, and all the camera could do was sit right down in front of them and grind away. And when they put the dancers in the set, they were so jammed together that they looked more like extras in a disaster movie fleeing some ten-story ape. It was so crowded that no one could do a high kick without doing serious damage to the set or another dancer. All they could do in the space they had was shuffle. So the wild Spanish dance that had been choreographed looked more like forty people trying to scrape dogshit off the bottoms of their shoes.

And, of course, the music track was recorded in advance and the singers and dancers had to mime to the track. It never did match up, but the budget called for only nine days of shooting. Imagine!

But my score was good, because I knew what instruments sounded good on those crude soundtracks and I scored accordingly. It wasn't something I'd thought out in advance. It was something I'd learned from just sitting in movie theaters.

I loved every minute of it. But when it was done, I went back to my studies and forgot about it.

All that's important about that movie is that that's when I met Wesley Ober. He was the juvenile in the movie. He sang passably well and he spotted me the first day on the set and asked me to work with him on synching his song. "Pretty Iberian señora, you'll never know how ador-a-ble you are-a."

Wesley had a bed, too. And Wesley also had a circle of friends that would open up a whole world for me.

I've known Wesley for over forty years. That's over two

generations. God, but he was handsome when I first met him. He had great style and was wonderfully social. He knew everyone worth knowing. It seems there were a lot of people worth knowing in those days. I can't think of ten I'd like to know now.

He was brilliant socially. He was an indifferent actor. He acted in the grand manner, just short of florid. But he didn't care, and, right to the end, he kept every rotten mannerism he learned in resident stock.

A "for instance"? . . . Well, love scenes. Instead of looking yearningly at the woman in his arms, he would strike a pose that made him look like a figure on an antique valentine. He would stretch his neck and angle his head away from the woman and towards the spotlight, and his eyes would grow moist. I think it was meant to convey yearning, but he gave the impression that he was slightly offended by the heroine's breath.

He knew he was a tepid actor, but he loved the life. He wasn't as obsessed by the stage as I was by music. He'd say to me, "How long do you intend to live? It won't be forever, chum, and you'll miss a lot of fun." And I'd get sententious and say that life was more than fun. And he'd laugh at me. He could never see that being serious about my music was my "fun."

But that disparity of spirit didn't keep us from becoming lovers. And I'll always be grateful to him for getting me out into the larger world. My life would have been a good deal different if he hadn't.

It was he who got me to Jack Warner, and it was I who got him into RKO. But that's another story. That's a little later.

My clearest memory of New York then? Let's see. Well, one could go anywhere . . . the Village, Harlem, the Lower East Side. One never had to worry about danger. And I remember glamour. I remember that people went about looking their best. It meant something. Things had a gloss, things had high-lights. . . .

Just to sit in Sardi's and watch the entrances. Lunt and Fontanne always entered in conversation—bright, animated. Cornell would come in in regal silence, and pause just on the edge of the dining room, like an empress. Hayes would enter modestly . . . like Marie Antoinette on her way to milk the cows. And so many more. They didn't do it for cheap effect. They did it to keep faith with their audiences. It's hard to realize now, but stars felt their obligations to their audiences and had some respect for the people who paid the money that made them stars.

Of course, there was a depression. The country was poor. What's that got to do with what I'm talking about? . . .

Young man, between your concern about my psychological makeup and the social condition of the nation, you're apt to completely miss the point of what I'm saying. At the risk of sounding conceited, I thought we were supposed to talk about me.

Then let us.

As I was saying . . . Wesley and I used to sit in Sardi's almost every night when we first met. We'd have dinner there after his show. He was in a comedy at the Broadhurst. Awful little piece of nonsense, but it did very well. Thalberg bought it for Shearer, but MGM never made it.

Who's Shearer?

Wait here a minute.

Here are four books on Broadway and Hollywood in the thirties. When you've read them, call me and we'll set up another appointment. Your questions make me feel like a relic. You read those books. Go see some old movies. You won't understand me until . . . well, until you look at some of the "artifacts" of my times.

You make me feel old. Go 'way. And don't look so crushed. I'm damned if I'll feel guilty because you didn't do your homework. But if I'm as old as some of your questions imply, I need a nap.

All right, come back Tuesday . . . if you've read those books.

# Billy Hicks

We have lots of time today. Move those swatch books and sit there. Let me get my glasses. I can never hear what I'm saying without my glasses.

My childhood? Of what possible interest could that be?

Well, it's not very interesting to me. But all right.

I grew up in a factory town, and as soon as I could I got out. I came to New York. That's not quite true. In a way, I had to leave. I was forced to.

Of course there's more, but . . .

Very well.

I was born in Schenectady. A dreary joint. It's a factory town up the Hudson. When I was a child it was dominated by General Electric—probably still is—and a locomotive plant and a mica plant. (I don't know. They did something or other with mica.) Near the mica plant the gutters were always deep in a kind of glittering confetti from the mica. But the whole town was sooty, the way places look in Buffet's pictures. Always dirty around the edges.

One grew up there either working for one of the factories or training to work in the factory. The point of life was to get a job and hold on for dear life, till one got a gold watch one was too old to hear tick.

Of course I sound bitter. It gobbled up everyone. The educational institutions were funded to produce more and better fodder for the factories . . . and they did. It was a closed loop. The factory hands begat babies that would grow to be more skilled than their parents. Then the kids were groomed to become their parents' betters. Both sides understood this, and when the children gained status they ignored their parents. It seemed right to everyone. The parents were resigned. Mine were even proud when their children became their betters. They bragged about it.

My two brothers became executives with General Electric and left our parents in that awful shack on Albany Street till I had enough to get them out of there.

But I couldn't do much for them, because they didn't want what I had to give. So I just sent them money and left them be. Maybe they didn't like the fact that my money came from what my Aunt May called "that sissy business."

Looking back, it all seems more awful than when I was living it. I thought memory cleared things up. My memories of Schenectady seem to have gotten grubbier.

I was a change-of-life child. I don't think I was supposed to happen, because my brothers were both in their teens when I was born, and they were just old enough to feel paternal about me.

I think I puzzled my mother. No, that's not right. Actually, I think she was afraid of me. I used to go up to her and she'd stare at me as if I'd come to give her some terrible news. When she tried to talk to me she stammered. She seemed to hate having me around. I was never hauled along to go shopping with her the way most kids are. Just as well. Perhaps she had forgotten how to take care of babies, or I hadn't been wanted, or perhaps I'd been a hard birth. Perhaps I wasn't my father's child. No matter. She avoided me, so my father and brothers provided all the affection, until . . .

How can I put this? From the very beginning I was an unusual child. I was too pretty, too soft. To be plain, I was effeminate.

There was never any way around that. And I was only comfortable with the nature I had.

My father and my brothers tried—oh, never harshly—to interest me in sports and cowboy pictures and whatever it is that little boys are supposed to do "normally." They never could, so the best they could do was give me what I said I wanted or needed and leave me alone.

I don't mean they shunned me or abandoned me, but there was no way they could participate in my life or interest me in theirs.

Books—except for the ones required by their courses at Union College—were anathema to them and, for them, music was all right . . . to dance to. I was always reading, always in a class play, always drawing, or at the movies. I loved school. I loved music.

Because they didn't mind, I wasn't made to mind that I was different. School activities were a good reason not to get home until my father and brothers did.

I can never remember my mother or father as anything but work-worn. Mother seemed shapeless in those dresses she got at Grant's. Father was either in overalls or brown trousers, the crotch around his knees. It's a picture I don't usually summon. That youth doesn't match up with what I want my clients to see. I'm not ashamed of it, but I've learned to shut up about it.

Lily Gusmin was my mentor in this business. As she used to say, "You've got to be classier than your clients. They're seldom sure of themselves. You must always be. And when it's your taste against theirs, you're going to have to outclass them. . . . Cut them down with that razor crease in your Dunhill trousers."

I think—no, I *know* there was great relief among my relatives when I started seeing a lot of girls in high school. But I saw them because I had more in common with them than with boys, that was all.

Of course I thought I was the only homosexual in the world. Well, that's not quite true. There was a man who wore blazing white suits in summer in that dirty city. He had a thin moustache and slicked hair. People pointed at him. I didn't know what they were laughing at, but I felt it had something to do with me. I remember him as being heavily powdered, but that's apt to be wrong. Perhaps he was just deathly pale.

But I *felt* I was the only homosexual. It's hard being something for which one doesn't even have a name. And I didn't for a long time. I used to wonder, What am I? I saw the boys in my class and longed for them, but I couldn't figure out what that vague aching was, and I couldn't recognize it in others. I couldn't see that anyone looked at me with the same longing.

I found out about sex in the streets. The first name I had for what I was, was "cocksucker." Must have been seven or eight. It was years before I heard "homosexual," more years till I heard the word "gay."

"Cocksucker" was an awful word the way they used it, but it meant that my condition was nameable. I knew I was awful, but I finally had a name for all those odd feelings. I wasn't nothing. I was awful, but I wasn't nothing.

I know now that what I longed for was intimacy, physical intimacy, but those feelings were as nameless as my homosexuality had been.

This seems weird to me now that I think about it, but when I was about seven I had this terrible need to be held. I knew my mother was out, as far as that went, so I would cuddle up to my brothers. They'd give me a hug, move away, and then give me a cheerful clip on the shoulder. Big, manly stuff, you know. But I had this awful need to be held and I didn't know what to do about it, until . . . I don't know why I was there, but I was alone in Central Park—Schenectady's Central Park—and I felt so lonely that I ached. So I looked around until I could find a tree that I could get my arms around and I went up and held it for dear life. And I just stood there and held on and bawled my eyes out. I pressed as hard as I could against that tree and bawled. I don't know what that tells you, but that's what I did.

It was nine more years till I was held by someone. It was Dick. Thank God for Dick. He was fourteen, I was sixteen. He seduced me, and when I think about our first time together I still tremble. My God, he seemed beautiful. My God, he was hung.

I met him in Woolworth's—the Bloomingdale's of Schenectady—and when we saw one another something passed between us that I now know was recognition . . . sexual recognition. We sniffed at one another from one end of that store to another, and then when he knew I was hooked, he drew me toward the rear entrance and waited in the street outside the door. I could see him standing there and I was terrified of going out, because I knew that if I did, something momentous would happen. Without consciously admitting it, I knew what I was heading toward.

I was standing near the oilcloth counter; I can still smell the stuff when I think of this. I stood inside the door and watched him and he stood outside growing impatient. And then he reached down and his hand pressed flat against his left thigh and I could see his cock outlined in his brown pants.

So I plunged. I went out to him. As I say, some come out of the closet; I came out of Woolworth's.

Neither of us had a place to go. He lived with his grandmother, and my mother might be home. So we went to the local graveyard, which was right in the middle of town. We didn't kiss. He just lay down and took out his cock. He put my hand on it, then he moved my head to it and said, "Put it in your mouth."

Then he unzipped me and took out my cock. Then he arranged us in a sixty-nine.

That moment still seems so natural, so right.

I never loved him, but I lived for him a long time.

I never knew where his parents were and never asked. I was incurious, because he seemed enough for me, all by himself. Children don't need pedigrees among themselves.

We met after school every day—or almost every day—and we would find places where we could be private. I can't remember much of what we ever said together.

Since my mother was incurious about me, it went on for several months. Mostly, I remember just touching and holding and sex.

I do remember the last time we met. We went to the movies. It was a weekday afternoon and the place was almost empty. We'd sit and hold one another's cocks and eat Necco Wafers, because you could eat them with one hand, right out of the package. Dick seemed upset, but I didn't ask why. As I said, we seemed incurious about one another. Finally, he told me what was bothering him. He told me he'd spent the day in court, and I remember feeling frightened by that. He said he'd been there to testify against a man with whom he'd had an affair for a long time.

Remember, he was fourteen. But he was very tall for his age, taller than I at sixteen. I have the impression he looked older than I. I'm not sure about that.

Dick and the man had driven into the country one day and parked. They'd gone into the woods and were having sex when they saw two policemen heading through the trees toward them. Dick must have been thirteen at the time. He had only just turned fourteen when I met him. When Dick saw the police he panicked and began yelling. The police ran to him and he began telling them he'd been taken there by the man against his will.

The man was arrested and jailed. That day, Dick had told his story in court and the man was sentenced to several years. I looked for the story in the *Gazette* the next day, and there was a piece about a man sentenced for corrupting the morals of a minor. They didn't give Dick's name. I think the man was twenty-two.

When I read that story, I became afraid about sex for the first time. I discovered that what had seemed so beautifully right and guiltless was a crime. The boy with whom I'd been sharing that odd Eden was somehow tarred by that awfulness, and a man was in jail for a long time for no more than I'd been doing.

That's when I went on guard. It never occurred to me that I would have sex or wanted sex with anyone but men, but I had my first lesson in the consequences of being my natural self. I was now not only awful, I was illegal.

I never questioned that. I accepted it. I thought they were right.

I never saw Dick again. That's not true. I saw him many years later and we had sex again.

Since I was left alone—not neglected, mind you, just left to myself—I was free to pursue what interested me. I've no idea why I decided I wanted to be an architect, but I remember that that was my dream in high school. Maybe I just liked the sound of the word. It does have a ring. Maybe I just wanted to be something different from all my classmates. But that's what I settled on, and my brothers supported me.

My father didn't have much idea of what an architect did, but when my brothers assured him that it was lucrative, he didn't seem as bothered as he was by his sense that it was an "arty" career.

I don't remember my mother having any opinion on the matter.

You don't have to point out the obvious, ducks. Of course I'm not an architect. Very obviously I'm not an architect.

Yes, I began studying, and I did well. My math wasn't all that good, but good enough.

It was so long ago that it hardly seems worth going into. And it's still a little painful. I'd stick it out now. I wouldn't run, but I did then.

Why shouldn't I tell you?

I got caught. The school found out I was gay. It wasn't Dean's fault.

We'd been lovers. That is, Dean and I were lovers. I was going to Union College. Let me think a moment. Yes.

Since I couldn't afford to go away to school, I began my training at Union College. I planned to try for a better school of architecture, but Union College was good enough to start with. The campus was right in the middle of Schenectady, so it meant that I could live at home and save. It also let me work a few hours a week. By then, my brothers were married, but they still managed a little money for me.

I met Dean in my second semester. He lived on campus in a frat house. Once we started being lovers, we were inseparable. I was like Crusoe with Friday. He was, too. He didn't know any other gay people either. Perhaps because we didn't, neither of us had ever learned to develop any disguises, protective coloring—whatever you want to call it. What I'm saying is that I guess we were pretty obvious together. That may be all right for straights, all that gazing and sighing and touching the young do, but at Union College in 1935 . . .

We were foolish enough to make love in Dean's room at the frat house. He shared the room, but we timed our sex so that his roomie would be at class or lab or practice.

I suppose it was bound to happen. Roomie came home and found us in bed. He just stared at us from the door. Didn't say a thing . . . just stared. Then he closed it. No word, no shocked noise, no sound from him.

About a week later I was crossing campus one night, coming from the library, and I was heading toward a gate onto Union Street. There were clusters of trees and shrubs on either side of the gate, and when I got almost to the gate, somebody said, "Billy." He sounded friendly, so I turned to see who, and the voice came from the shrubs and said, "Over here." There was no threat in the voice. No reason for me to feel alarmed. And it wasn't a time when we walked in fear. Imagine being so trusting today. So I went toward the voice.

There were four of them. One was Dean's roommate. I thought I'd seen the others around on campus, but I wasn't sure. Besides, it was dark there.

They weren't shy. They told me what they wanted, and what they'd do if I didn't give it to them. They didn't understand that what I did with Dean was different, that I chose to make love to Dean.

I tried to tell them. They didn't bother to listen. After all, what's a fag? We'll do it with anyone. We don't discriminate. We're after anything that walks.

I blew all of them and they went away.

I sat there in the dark crying for a while. What was worse was that I thought they did have the right to do what they did, because I was gay.

I thought of Dean, but I couldn't go to him. They'd made me afraid. I knew that if I went and found them doing anything to Dean, I wouldn't be able to do anything but run away.

Imagine, my dear, I thought we were the only two fairies in the whole world.

All I could do that night was go home and try to wash it off.

The next day I was walking to class and Dean was coming toward me. When he saw me, he turned off the walk and ran across the grass. He looked so frightened. Poor baby. I couldn't stand the idea of knowing what might already have happened to him. So I didn't run after him.

I saw him from time to time for a few weeks—just from a distance—and then he seemed to be completely gone.

I stuck it out. I was only called on to "service" someone from time to time, but I guess the word was getting around. I was a handy—what would you call it?—receptacle?

I rarely went to any campus parties, but I did that spring. I went to one at a frat house where some of the guys had been nice to me.

You know the parties . . . all beer and brag and an assortment of deb types. I don't know who started what happened, but late in the party I was caught upstairs in the house coming out of the john.

Two of them took me into one of the bedrooms where there were two others. This time it was sodomy they wanted. I fought for a while, but, Jesus, what good did it do? They began, and then there were others.

All I could do was go inert, to shut off. All I could do was lie there and be used. But I became aware of screaming. It went on and on, it seemed. Then I was alone for a while, and I lay where they'd left me and wondered if I'd been screaming. But I hadn't been. It had been some co-ed.

One of the drunker boys had brought his date up to the room for a peek. I guess he'd overestimated her sophistication, because when she saw what was going on she started to scream. She'd run from the house screaming, and she'd run right into some teachers. They came back to the house with her. They found me where I'd been left on the bed.

It all came out. They were allowed to stay in school. I was asked to leave. How did they put it? I'd become a cause for scandal and my flagrant behavior had undoubtedly contributed to what happened, perhaps even incited the incident.

That was that.

There were some medical problems, which I ignored at first. No, I didn't ignore them. I was too ashamed to go to a doctor.

How would I explain it? I finally went to a doctor in Albany. I felt very humiliated.

I kept it all from my family.

When I was told by the school that I would have to leave, I just stayed home for a few days. I said I was ill. I'd get the mail every morning, so I got the letter from the school saying I'd been expelled and that the tuition wasn't refundable. All that hard-earned money. But the letter was an end—it told me I had to go. Not just from school, but from home. I understood that I could not survive there. They'd get me. One way or another they'd get me.

I sorted through my things, sold my high-school class ring and a few other odds and ends, and got ready to come to New York.

No, I can't remember a thing I felt. All I could concentrate on was getting out, getting away.

Plans? Not a one. I wanted out of Schenectady. I came to New York because it looked good in the movies, and everything always came out all right in the movies.

Not much of a preparation for life in the Big Town. But I guessed that I could get lost in the city, and my guess was right.

But I found out that I didn't want to get quite as lost as I got. But I'm jumping ahead. . . .

Would you like some coffee? I'll ask Charlotte to get us some.


I hit New York about as dumb as anyone who ever arrived here. I must have been quite a sight getting off that Greyhound bus. I had a fifteen-cent haircut and my mother still bought me clothes as if she expected me to grow into them. I had Aunt Edna's suitcase, the one she'd bought for her honeymoon in 1905. Big old brown thing. Everything about me said "hick." My idea of grooming was a jar of Arrid, and I put that on with a trowel. I'd never even heard of a nail brush.

Remember, this was 1935. It was the days before one could pee on a bus, so my first stop in New York was the tea room.

Normally, one's future isn't decided in a tea room. Mine was. Twice.

That's where Billy Hicks was born, so to speak. Unfortunately, a good fairy and a bad fairy attended that birth. I met the bad one first.

Rube that I was, I set my suitcase down near the door of the men's room and went to pee. The man at the next urinal was playing with himself and he was hard. God knows, he wasn't attractive, but I was fascinated—also appalled—at what I was seeing. But I stood and watched. Apparently I watched a long time.

When I could tear myself away, I looked around and my bag was gone. I just stood and stared at the empty space. I couldn't believe it. Have you ever had anything stolen? Then you know the feeling.

I must have made some kind of noise, because the man who'd been showing hard tucked it in and came over to me.

Anyway, he was Henry. He was very definitely a Henry, certainly not a Hank. And within an hour after arriving, I was being kept . . . so to speak.

Henry wasn't a good fairy or a bad fairy. I guess you'd call him the midwife, because he got me out of the Greyhound depot and into New York.

The depot used to be up on Fifty-first Street, right across from the Hellinger Theater. It was right in the middle of what I thought of as New York. It was tourist New York.

We walked south, and I'll never forget the sight. It was just as I'd seen it in the Movietone newsreels on New Year's Eve, but all in color—the Wrigley sign and the Astor Hotel and the Capitol Theater and, way down at the end, the Paramount and the Times Building with its news sign running around the building spelling out news about Roosevelt.

Do you remember Garland's arrival in Oz? That was me . . . all eyes, and oohs and ahs. When I saw *The Wizard of Oz* a few years later, I knew exactly how she felt. I loved everything about that movie but the end. She wanted to go home. I didn't. I always thought she was a fool to leave Oz. I never did. I stayed in New York.

Anyway, Henry led me away down what was still the "Great White Way." And it was—it was a white blaze of lights. Henry lived in what he called Murray Hill. Actually, it was on the edge of the garment district, somewhere between there and Murray Hill. A funny little walk-up, a warren of rooms. They were clean and tidy as a doll's house and decorated in a poor facsimile of a Ginger Rogers musical.

Why do I want to make Henry sound foolish? He wasn't. He was kind, but he was a good deal older than I—probably thirty-five—and that made him seem like an old man to me. But he fed me, and bought me some clothes, and gave me a place to stay.

And he never laid a hand on me. He'd watch me. He watched me like a kid watches a cake.

Henry helped me dope out what the want-ads meant in the newspapers—all that peculiar shorthand—and I'd trudge off every morning and look for work. I'd join the long lines and wait. There was a lot of unemployment in Schenectady, so what I saw in New York didn't look unusual to me. It was sad and depressing, but it wasn't unfamiliar.

And every time my job-hunting took me near the Greyhound depot, I'd pop into the tea room. I was a hick, but I was a fast learner. I never dared to do anything, but I loved looking. Also, there was the weird comfort of finally knowing I wasn't alone. Here lived other fairies.

And that's how I met the bad fairy. He even looked the part.

He was a furtive little guy. He seemed to be there every time I was—usually around noon. Small, wiry, very jittery, with shifty eyes. He was always in a suit and a hat. Men wore hats in those days. And he had a wedding band.

Maybe I was to blame for what happened. He may have thought I'd given him some signal, because one day he followed me out of the station. He walked behind me for a bit and then he came up to me and said, "Do you have someplace to go?" I was appalled. To be honest, I found him repulsive. That must have showed when I looked at him. He looked as if I'd hit him and he backed off. He said, "You trade?" (I'd never heard the expression.) "You're just some of that trashy trade, aren't you? Don't give me that innocent look. Who'd pay for you? You're scum. I wouldn't touch you."

Our act got quite a bit of attention from people. Since I couldn't figure out what was going on, I just stood there like an idiot while he raved. When I understood what was happening, I ran . . . ran straight down Broadway as if the devil was after me.

Oh, the bad fairy is important.

You see, a week later I got the bright idea of going over to General Electric on Lexington Avenue and seeing if they had any work. G.E. was home away from home. A haven. For once, my luck was with me and I was hired for the mailroom. Someone had just been fired and the boss was out sick, so I went to work right away. That was a Wednesday. The mailroom boss came back the following Monday. You guessed. The boss was my angry friend from the Greyhound depot.

Unfortunately, I'd gotten ahead of myself financially and moved from Henry's to the Y the day I got the job. So, you see, I felt I couldn't quit.

For a few days the boss treated me very coolly, acted very reserved. Naturally, I thought his intention was to have his way with me, ravage my then-sylphlike body.

I remember thinking at the time that he behaved just like an old cat I was raised with. The poor old cat was arthritic, so it could only go after the sure thing, like an aging mouse or an injured fly. She would have to wait till her target was only a whisker away before she'd move. . . .

He was like that. He stayed quiet, sniffed out the situation. He probably checked to be sure I wasn't some big shot's kid or nephew before he went to personnel.

Anyway, a week after they hired me, they fired me. I was called into personnel and they said I was through as of that day. I said they'd told me I had a month's trial, and the personnel man said that if I must know, I was being let go for making an obscene proposal to another young man in the shipping department.

Of course, I took it. I was getting used to it. It seemed right. It seemed like I was getting what I deserved for being a pervert.

I went back to the Y and had a good cry and felt sorry for myself for a while. And then I thought, I'm getting shat on right and left for being queer, and I'm not having any fun out of it. So, I showered and walked from the Y on Thirty-fourth up to the Greyhound depot.

Yes, I know I wasn't doing too well there, but it was the only place I knew where gay people went. I think I also thought that if I ran into that slimy little bastard I'd beat the shit out of him.

He wasn't there, but the good fairy was there. The good fairy was Teddy.

Yes, the Teddy who was my lover for twenty years.

Teddy was standing at a urinal, and he rather frightened me. He had bleached hair with a deep wave in it, and he wore the kind of clothes I'd never seen on a man. Very tight, skin-fitting.

Men in the thirties wore commodious trousers, almost like culottes. But there stood Teddy, with no ass to speak of, poured into his trousers.

My first reaction was revulsion at this awfully feminine man, but I caught sight of myself in the mirror and there was that round face of mine with the cocksucker lips and the shaped

brows—unplucked, but very Norma Shearer—and I knew that I
had more in common with him than anyone I'd ever met. I
thought, That's what I am. I'm queer. But I'm not alone.

Teddy rolled his eyes at me, and I went and stood next to him.
He said, "My place?" and I said yes.

My God, was that a night . . . and a day. We were like a couple
of kids together. I was about twenty, but I remember having my
childhood with Teddy. Children are very old in Schenectady.

It was Teddy who led me to Lily Gusmin. It was Teddy who
gave me a life. Meeting Teddy meant all the difference in the
world. The only bad thing about what happened was that I took
Teddy away from Bob—Bob Regal. He's never really forgiven
me. Imagine, forty-four years of a grudge. In a way, I don't
blame him. He's never really had anyone else.

After Teddy, Bob never had another lover as such. Oh, the
usual run of affairs—usually with married men—but never
another lover.

Meeting Teddy meant all the difference in the world. You see,
between Teddy and Lily, I became a New Yorker, and Lily gave
me my career.

# Robert Regal

Who hasn't heard Billy's college horror story? Billy trots it out every time there's an evening of suffering. You know, those evenings when they sit around like Camp Fire Girls telling stories to frighten themselves with. Billy's got that college of his, and Wesley has that dreary Southern town, and that tale about Lulubelle, or whatever the hell her name was.

My childhood? I was born in Philadelphia in 1911 and raised in Wilkes-Barre. I was the second of five children. Three boys, two girls. I don't remember much of it. There's not much to remember. I told you I wasn't a very good subject for this project of yours. Being "colorful" like the others is not my stock in trade.

Of course I knew what I was. I knew early and I was smart enough to hide it. I kept it out of my life. It's only been an occasional indulgence. I'm not a career faggot.

My brother Ed was the firstborn. He started screwing girls when he was eleven. Me? I didn't do anything. I studied. I worked hard.

We weren't rich. I always had to earn my way. I gave money into the house as soon as I was able to work. I was eleven when I had my first job at March's Grocery over on Bellevue. Fifteen cents an hour.

We were Lutheran. I was known as a good boy. We prayed at home. Every night before supper. And then we'd eat. Dad liked it quiet at the table. And then I'd go up and study. Straight A's. All through school, straight A's. And they're what got me a scholarship. Unfortunately, I couldn't afford to take it.

Why'd Wesley mention Arthur to you? He would. Jesus, he's a gossip.

Arthur was just a boy I went to school with. I didn't know any better then. I was a good child from a very religious home. Arthur was . . . well, his people were dirt poor. Lived over on Oak. Awful neighborhood. Poor Italians, mostly, but blacks too, even then.

But Arthur was always clean. His name was really Arturo, but he changed it to fit in. The kids were cleverer than their parents. Not like now, when even stars think it's so great and brave to be ethnic.

Arthur had nothing but hand-me-downs, but he was always clean. And he was a little sissy. You know, slightly pretty, with those big dark eyes. He sat two rows up from me and he was always turning around to look at me. You couldn't help noticing. Miss McAffey was always asking him, "What are you looking at, Arthur?"

I don't know why he picked on me. I certainly didn't encourage him. Mother wouldn't have let me play with him, and he wasn't very smart, so what was the point.

We were about twelve . . . because it was the sixth grade. Every time I'd go to the bathroom, Arthur would be there. It seemed that way, anyway. I suppose he had a crush on me. As I said, he wasn't very smart.

One day when there wasn't anyone else in the bathroom, he got an erection. Of course I looked at it, and I got a little excited. But I certainly never egged him on. I let him touch me, and he got ideas and then there was no stopping him.

I never touched him. I'd put my hands in my pockets and let him play with me, but I never touched him. And I certainly never meant him any harm.

You must remember that I was from a strongly religious home. God was very much a presence in that house. . . .

Your question implies I should feel quilty about what happened. I resent that. What I did was a very natural thing for me to do. I told my father what was going on. I still don't see how I could have done otherwise. I told my father about Arthur.

There was no great harm. Arthur was just transferred. Actually, he went to a much better school.

As you see, there's much less to the story than Wesley led you to believe.

I'm surprised Billy had the gall to tell you about Teddy.

Yes, that's still a sore point. But I'm damned if I'm going to let them tell you only their side. I have a side, too.

Teddy and I were lovers and Billy took him away from me. And Teddy was all I had. All I ever wanted.

I met Teddy in 1933.

After I'd graduated from high school, I went to Philadelphia to work, so I could take night courses in accounting at Penn. I finished there at the start of the Great Depression. I'd earned excellent grades. The top people in a class stood a better chance, so I didn't feel as hopeless about getting a job as some. But I was still worried.

I applied for work at Price Waterhouse in Philadelphia, but they didn't have anything. I apparently impressed them. They called New York. There were two jobs there. So I went up and I got one of them.

Price Waterhouse was the best. Sixteen-fifty a week. Good money, then. We worked hard, very hard. That was fine. That's what I wanted.

I couldn't work for that firm and behave promiscuously. My God, they would have . . . I can't even imagine what they would have done.

I just worked and learned my way around. I wanted to get ahead. Not having a wife wasn't too much of a liability, because most of the other young men weren't married either. Almost impossible on that wage in those times. So that was all right. It was considered rude to ask if a man was married. In some ways a man was considered a fool to take on a wife with the economy what it was. Sure, the situation suited me.

I can't see that how I took care of my sexual needs is any of your business. If it's gossip you want, talk to Wesley.

I will tell you about Teddy. I know they think I'm a fool. I know it's forty-four years. If I'd had a limp for that long, would it be any better?

Teddy was a problem for me, but I cared for him, cared very much. The problem was that he was . . . well, inappropriate. He had bright blond hair. It wasn't bleached, but it certainly looked it. He looked almost like a girl with that hair. And he was a wraith. Willowy, you'd call it.

I met him in Greenwich Village. It had been a good day, and I was walking uptown from our offices down on Pine. I'd stopped to look in a shop window on Sixth Avenue and Teddy came up and spoke to me. He said, "That's real Chippendale. Isn't it beautiful?"

I knew that he was—well, gay—the minute I looked at him. I wanted to run. I was sure that someone from the office would see us and think I knew him.

I'll never know where I got the courage to walk off with him, but I did. That's how we began.

It wasn't easy then. Two men. People noticed. My God, when I see men actually holding hands.

No, I don't think it's right, and I'd appreciate not being convinced it is.

We didn't live together. That would have been impossible. My God, in those days there were only three restaurants in the Village where people like us were welcome. When we could go out, that's where we went, to one of those restaurants.

Teddy worked for an awful woman named Lily Gusmin. Lily Gusmin was really Rose Mingus. She'd transposed the syllables in her last name. She was hot stuff in the decorating business in the thirties.

Frankly, when I first met him I thought that Teddy was one of those layabouts, and I was certainly in no position to do anything for him financially, I had all I could do to look after myself. But I found out he made fairly good money for those days.

He sewed for her. He was one of those people who could make anything on a sewing machine. He made his own clothes. Awful, swishy stuff.

I told him once, "I won't go out with you, with you looking like some goddamned whore." I apparently hurt him, and I'm sorry for that. But I worked for a very conservative organization, and there was no sense in rubbing anyone's nose in what we were.

Teddy bought a suit that he wore when we went out. It helped some.

Teddy was the one who liked to go out. I was quite happy to stay in. I hated walking into those restaurants. Every time the door opened, everybody would turn around and stare. I could just hear them saying, "There are two more of us." I wasn't one of them, not in the sense they meant.

What made it worse was that Teddy knew everyone. I'd get furious with him. He'd table-hop. I told him that I'd be damned if I'd go out to dinner with him and spend most of the time alone at the table. But he'd make up to me and . . . and he could make me laugh. He could be very funny. And I don't mean campy-funny. He had a real sense of humor.

We were together for almost two years.

I met a lot of people through Teddy. A lot of them I could do without, but it was a social life of sorts.

The only evenings I couldn't stand were those ones at Lily's. Ten men and Lily, with her playing queen of the fags . . . queen of the queens. All that dancing attendance. Everything they said seemed to have some sexual innuendo, everything was said with a lot of hand-waving.

Teddy could make Lily laugh. She had a coarse laugh. I used to wonder if she laughed that way with her clients. She had the top names of that time as clients. She'd gotten Cole Porter's wife as a client, and that was her making. Miss Mingus became a big society decorator.

I suppose she was good at it. I don't know much about such things.

I met Carl and Wesley at her place. I could at least talk to them without all that la-di-da crap. And they had jobs that I could understand. Wesley was very well established by then, and Carl was obviously making some inroads in the music business.

Then Billy showed up, and I could see right off what was going on. I wasn't blind. Billy was all over Teddy, and Teddy did nothing to discourage him. Teddy never did have any sense of proper limits. I let it go the first time, but when Billy showed up again, I let Teddy have it.

I didn't beat around the bush. I told him—straight out—that I knew something was going on between them. It was all well and good for Teddy to behave the way he did, but he must have some concern for me, my position. If he could have just toned things down. Frankly, it frightened me to be seen with him. He always seemed to be high on something. I wanted to make him see that I didn't have any choice about being discreet.

I'll never understand how he could say he loved me and then in the very next breath say that he wanted to stop seeing me.

He told me about Billy when I confronted him. He said he loved me, but we didn't have any future. What an awful, unfeeling thing to say.

Teddy made all the difference in the world to me, but I

couldn't . . . I couldn't place myself in jeopardy. If he wanted someone like Billy whom he could paw in public, that just wasn't me. He did indeed have the wrong person.

It all seems so easy for you kids these days. Do what you want and the hell with the rest of the world. It wasn't that way in my day. If you were smart you hid the fact that you were "that way." You had to. The alternatives could be pretty nasty, including prison. If you don't understand that, you won't understand a word I'm saying.

No, I couldn't have gone into one of those—what's your phrase?—"accepting professions." What's professional about being a chorus boy or a seamstress or a hairdresser? And that's what the alternative was. It still is. Every doctor or lawyer or teacher I know still plays it safe. They'd be dead if they didn't. That's the way it was. That's the way it is.

I tried very hard to make Teddy see where I stood. I talked to Wesley about it. I even went to see Carl. Their advice wasn't much help. How could I just let Teddy be, and let his affair with Billy blow over?

Jesus! People laughed at Teddy. We'd be walking through the Village and people would actually laugh.

Wesley said to let the Billy-and-Teddy thing play itself out.

My God, I'd given myself to Teddy, even though he was the way he was.

I don't know why I'm going on about this. You know what happened. Undoubtedly, Billy has told you about Teddy and how "idyllic" it was for all those years. If we're telling tales out of school, ask Billy what happened with Teddy when the war broke out.

# Wesley Ober

I suppose Bob thought he was letting the cat out of the bag mentioning Carrie Sue. Some cat. Some bag.

After fifty years, the story seems almost apocryphal, even to me, and it happened to me. But that was another me, then . . . young and pretty enough to play an angel for Griffith.

If you want, you can close your eyes, because the story's pretty unbelievable if you try to connect it to the way I look now.

I was born and grew up on a tobacco farm in North Carolina. The town was called Catch Mills, and the name was nothing more than a sign on a place that was a gas station, general store, and post office, all in one. Oh, yes, and up the road there was a smith, because there were still a lot of horses around.

Catch Mills is near Raleigh and Durham. That is, it's about as far from one as the other. I even went to a one-room schoolhouse. How's that for a touch of Americana?

It's all tobacco land. It's a crop that sucks all the good out of the land, but my dad did pretty well at it. Well enough to raise me and my six sisters. But not well enough to get us accepted into a single good home in Raleigh or Durham.

Ma might have been lots more social if she'd married differently. But she had to marry Pa when she got pregnant with Madeline. Pa was a looker when he was young. Ma was pretty, in a vague sort of way. We all came in pretty rapid succession, right through to Liane, the youngest. All those girls. Ma liked having them around. Me and Pa she always grouped as "men."

My earliest memory of her is her surrounded by girls, and her saying to me, "Go find your pa. See if he can find some use for you. I don't know what to do with you." She never scolded me, no matter what I did. She seemed to accept that men made messes, and whenever I did something wrong she'd simply say,

"Scoot!" and the last thing I'd hear as I ran off was, "Men!"

So I spent a lot of time trailing after Pa, who didn't seem to mind one way or the other. Every so often he'd try and teach me something, and when he'd see I was bored, he'd just stop. Once he said to me, "Looks like you're going to be a fancy britches. Well, you got the looks and you could do worse."

Even when I left home all Ma said was, "Probably for the best. Not much around here for someone like you." And Pa said, "Where you going?" I told him Norfolk, and he said, "Watch your money." Never did learn to do that.

Anyway, I grew up poor but pretty. All my sisters were beautiful, but I had a little something special. What I had was the fact that I didn't give a damn about much. I'm sorry to say I was pretty useless to Pa. The girls were more help than I was. Not that I wasn't manly, but I learned early that there was some kind of premium on being good-looking. I had all the girls after me . . . *and* a few of the boys.

I could screw anything. After all, I got started on melons.

Best screw you ever had. You go out in the field on a hot day and get a ripe one. You bore a hole in the end and fuck it.

And that's the way I felt about fucking . . . just so many warm holes, until Bernard.

Bernard was a neighbor boy.

Something special happened with Bernard. His father had the next farm over. I knew that Bernard was special to me, but it was a long time before I knew how.

Anyway, I'm forgetting Carrie Sue. She was society. Well, Raleigh society, anyway. Her mother owned a newspaper. I met her in high school when I was invited to join the all-county school choir.

Carrie Sue was a crotch watcher, and this was before men started stuffing it all up into those Jockey shorts. If it made any impression hanging there, Carrie Sue noticed. I got noticed.

The boys in my school used to tease me. They called me "nigger meat." So I captivated Carrie Sue. She always said she'd lost her heart to me. If that were true, you'd have to give her a cardiogram in her cooze. She always did have a fuzzy idea about her anatomy.

There was always talk about her, usually connected with her liking for the duskier members of the community, but nobody talked too loud about her, because her mother had power. And it was real power in a small community. For all her airs of gentility, her mother, Miss Catherine, was a despot. A smiling one, but a despot.

I screwed Carrie Sue a few times. In the past, this had always been treated as a kind of pastime. Most of the girls didn't take me seriously, because they knew there was no future with me. They wanted good providers, and it didn't look like I'd amount to much. With Carrie Sue it was different. I provided what she wanted, and she was used to getting what she wanted.

I didn't mind much one way or another when she said she wanted to speak to her mama about me. She said that she had been planning to go to Bryn Mawr, but she didn't have much taste for the idea. Her mama wanted it. She wanted to marry me, and her mama could spend the money for her education on me. That was fine by me. Carrie Sue wasn't a bad sort, and the offer was the best that had ever come my way.

We were fairly poor, and I didn't have much purpose; in the world I knew, marrying Carrie Sue would make me a prince.

So, I met Mama—Miss Catherine, that is—and she eyed me like something she'd just plucked off Carrie Sue's pubic hair. My looks cut no ice with Mama. But Miss Catherine was too smart to say a flat *no* to anyone as stubborn as her daughter. So, as they say, Miss Catherine went along with the gag, even saying that if we'd give it some time, she'd send us both off to college.

I had no idea what I'd study, but college meant a lot in those days. People would say things like, " You know Norma's boy, he went to college." People were impressed.

Carrie Sue acted dumb, because it was worth a girl's life to let a man know she had a brain. She used to quote her deportment teacher, who'd say to the girls, "Put a little fi-ah and sparkle in yo' eyes, darlin's. Don't sit there gazin' off into space like a Northrin woman." There's the making of a belle for you.

The arrangement seemed to be going splendidly. Carrie Sue and I were both very happy, if for very different reasons. Actually, as things stood, she had me and I had Bernard.

I say that because, while Carrie Sue was deciding she was in love with me, I went and fell in love with Bernard. We'd been having sex for a long time, and since it was beyond anything I knew about, it never occurred to me that I loved Bernard until he told me I did. And he said he loved me. I didn't argue with him, because when he said it, I knew he was right. It explained so much, including why I thought of Bernard when I was screwing Carrie Sue.

I just accepted the fact. I couldn't see any great problems. Even if I married Carrie Sue, Bernard would still be near, and I certainly couldn't marry Bernard.

As things were going, everybody could have had what they wanted, except that Miss Catherine didn't want a farmer's boy for her princess.

Miss Catherine had lines everywhere, so I wasn't surprised when she found out about Bernard and me. God knows, we spent enough time together—every moment we could. How she found out's not important. She found out.

Anyway, I was called to her house while Carrie Sue was out of town visiting cousins. There sat Miss Catherine with Father Costello. (I'd had sex with him a few times, and I've often wondered if he didn't put the finger on me.)

Miss Catherine gave quite a performance, all outraged virtue and community conscience, and a tear or two for her poor baby's deceived feelings. The gist was that I was to get my ass out of town, fare paid, to spare the town a scandal and to save Carrie Sue's sensitivities. I was to spare her baby's sensitivities by hauling ass out of there and writing to Carrie Sue that I could not go through with the wedding. They left the details of the excuse to me.

I stood there. I certainly wasn't overwhelmed at losing Carrie Sue, but I thought, "I'm not going alone. The only thing I'll miss will be my family and Bernard, especially Bernard." So, I upped my "going" price. I wanted the money so I could take Bernard with me.

I knew I wasn't much good to Pa, and marrying the girls off would be no problem for him. All except the youngest had beaus. If it wasn't to be Carrie Sue for me, there was no future for me in Catch Mills. As I said, leaving was no great problem, and the sooner the better.

I got cash from Miss Catherine and went home to tell Pa I was leaving and walked over to tell Bernard.

How he cried. Just sobbed and sobbed. He couldn't go. I did my damnedest to convince him. I wanted him. But I began to see that I could hurt him badly. All he knew was there in Catch Mills. He cared about home. My God, how I wanted him, but I knew I could damage him if I took him away from there. He was afraid. As I said, his family and the farm were all he knew. Odd, it was all I knew too, but I figured there had to be something out there. I knew I wouldn't fall off the edge of the world. Bernard was sure he would. Christ, I felt sorry for us. I think I would have married him, if it had even been thinkable then. So we just sat back of his daddy's barn, clinging for dear life, and crying.

I went home to pack, and my sister Madeline came up to my room. Madeline was my oldest sister. I was the fourth of the children. She was very no-nonsense, very commonsensical, and it bothered her terribly when she had her "visions." She'd get glimpses of the future and be furious about it. She said that "sensible women didn't get involved in such nonsense." But she had them all through her life. She was right about me.

Anyway, she came in and stood there watching me pack for a while. Finally, she asked me what I was going to do, and I said I didn't have any idea. I was just going. That's the way kids left home in those days—just up and out—so there wasn't any great stir about my leaving. Then she stood there some more, looking at me very intently. When she figured out exactly what she wanted to say (that was always her way), she said, "I watch you in town. You love being looked at. You're a strutter. You know people are looking, and how that suits you. Doesn't it? You may as well go on the stage. You may as well get paid for doing what you like to do best. It doesn't make sense, but I keep 'seeing' you on a stage. So go ahead and try. Nothing to lose. I won't tell Pa till you have some success. If you don't, nothing lost."

And that's how it started. That's why I tried the theater.

Yes, I saw both of them—Bernard and Carrie Sue—about thirty years later, not at the same time.

I'd had quite a success in _____ A lovely play with a charming leading lady. Her last Broadway show. I did three years on Broadway with it, and two more on the road. It was a lovely annuity.

I never understood actors who get bored with plays. I'm from the old school, where you set your performance down to the last detail and just go ahead and do it. I always tried to give the audience my best. These people who "do their own thing" often do nothing for the audience. . . .

Anyway, Bernard came backstage during the run, and he looked good. Thin, wiry, as he always was. Full head of hair. I was so happy to see him, but he kept apologizing for himself, for being a hick, for probably being boring to an important actor like me. That was sad, but he was proud of me. He paid me the best compliment he knew how to give about my acting. He said, "I could understand every word you said, even way up in the balcony."

I wasn't as happy to see Carrie Sue. She breezed into my dressing room, all simp and drawl, and she came right up, hugged me, and put her leg right between mine. Then she stood back and said, "You haven't changed. I want'chall to mee' ma husband. Ah bin Mrs. So-and-so since whenever." I looked at him and I said, "You're to be congratulated." I even managed to leave the question mark off my comment. She was wearing some flimsy yellow-green thing and she was fat, the kind that ripples. She looked like talking Jell-O. Lemon-lime. And I'd wanted to be her prince.

Being a faggot is not without its rewards. . . .

Where was I? Oh, yes. I left home and I went on up to Norfolk. I didn't know a damned thing about Norfolk, except that it was on the map and Catch Mills wasn't, and it was in bigger letters on the map than either Raleigh or Durham, so I thought it must be important. It was the days of touring stock—pretty much all gone, now—and there were two stock companies in town. I went to see both, and I decided to try the Classical Performers Company because the leading man looked gay to me.

He had a lovely, ripe name: Desmond Crownshield.

I wonder now where I got the gall, but I went back after the show and got into Desmond's dressing room, and Desmond got into my pants, and I got into Classical Performers. I loved the life right from the start. It suited my lazy nature. I could learn lines in two or three sittings, and the rooster in me gave me flair on stage. I did two seasons with them, and we were booked on a swing of big Southern towns, so my country drawl wasn't too great a disadvantage, even in Shakespeare.

But I learned. I had a fast ear and I learned to speak crisply, and oil my mouth with spit, get heard in the cheap seats. I also learned some bad habits, and for the life of me I've never been able to shake them.

We were in Atlanta doing six weeks of rep when the juvenile's agent said he'd gotten him a screen test with Famous Players-Lasky in New York. He and I were having a bit of a thing, so when he went to New York during a layoff, I went along.

His name was ——————, but he didn't become a big star at Twentieth till talkies.

But that's how I got up North, up to New York. . . .

* * *

Yes, I agree. Bob can be very spiky. That's probably in the nature of his business, being an accountant and all. You see, I've known him so long that I can't even judge any more whether he's a nice person or not. By now, that doesn't make any difference. In one way or another, he's been part of my life for over forty years. He can be troublesome, and I can be furious with him, but you get to a point where you can't give up some people, because you can't give up that much of your past.

Give Bob time, and I'll butter him up a little about your project. Bear with him. He'll come round. You're a new experience for him.

# PART 3

## Overture for the Thirties

The thirties were terrible. America was in a depression. The trusted institutions and leaders had failed. So, with extraordinary unanimity, Americans anchored their hopes to a new President, Franklin Delano Roosevelt. They saw Roosevelt as a Gibraltar of the spirit. As one observer said of him, "He must have been psychoanalyzed by God." That would have been a fine preparation for a man who set out to do something about the forty million impoverished of this nation. Roosevelt carved the statistic on the American consciousness when he said, "I see one third of a nation ill-housed, ill-clad, ill-nourished."

In a 1932 interview in the *Saturday Evening Post,* the great British economist, John Maynard Keynes, when asked if there had even been anything like the Depression, replied, "Yes. It was called the Dark Ages." William Manchester in his book *The Glory and the Dream* sums the era up by writing, "Seen in perspective, the Depression appears to have been the last convulsion of the Industrial Revolution, creating a hiatus before the technological revolution."

Historians still argue about the era, but no matter what caused the Depression, America fell deeply ill from an economic malaise that struck individuals and industry alike.

For gay people, the thirties must have been as economically punishing, but almost nothing is known about how gays as a group lived in that period.

When gay people were even heard about, it was in the pages of psychiatric journals, annals of jurisprudence, or the news columns that chronicled sexual transgressions, but usually in such veiled terms that readers were hard put to know why the person had been sentenced to five years in jail.

Judging by such historical "invisibility," it is possible to

53

assume that most gay people in the thirties must have lived by the assumption that society was right about them: They were criminally despicable. Thus, by their acceptance of "guilty as charged," roughly ten percent of the population endured and survived only by becoming an unseen army.

Many hid in the general culture by associating with "cover girls" and "fag hags" or even by marrying. Those who were admittedly but not flagrantly gay could become public figures, usually in fashion and in allied fields. After all, who would be threatened by a "seamstress" or makeup man or hairdresser, no matter of how high an order?

Those gays who were politicians, preachers, priests, lawyers, doctors, athletes, or whatever hid their sexuality, as most still do.

Gays lived without a literature, a means of communication to serve their interests and needs, or any sense of community.

Since they could not share fully in the culture of the decade, they created underground enclaves in which they formed their own culture, even evolving their own sense of humor, "camp."

In the pages that follow, the reader will not find our quartet of interviewees singing a song of their times, because they were not truly part of those times. They couldn't be.

Their problems in the thirties were not the dominant ones of the period, they were the more particular ones of making a life and career without incurring the moral wrath of the people who wished that gays, like the Depression, would go away or at least stay out of sight.

# PART 4

## "Play, Orchestra, Play"*

---

\*Noel Coward's hit song for the 1936 production of **Tonight at 8:30**

# Carl Mason

Lily Gusmin was probably the funniest woman I ever met. How she loved the boys. I was younger than you—twenty-five or so—when I was a regular at her place. I'd met a dancer, Frank or some such name, who was dancing in a musical called *Shady Lady*. And before you ask, a "shady lady" was a woman whose reputation was somewhat under a cloud. Frank met Lily because she had some money in the show.

At all events, he took me up to Lily's one evening for one of what she used to call her "boys' nights."

No, there was nothing condescending about that. She was a wonderful hostess and never patronizing. We were good company for her. Lily could tell a story with the best of them, and she always had gin when most of us were too poor to buy it. It was the first year of repeal and we felt obliged to drink, I suppose because it had become a classy thing to do during Prohibition. Cole's wife, Linda, had taught Lily to make the best martini in Manhattan.

I know the name is not much used these days, but I always think of the city as Manhattan. In the thirties the word had an aura of glamour. Remember, we were all expatriates at Lily's. We'd all fled places like Dubuque, East Armpit, Des Moines . . . Well, you get the idea. I'd come for the music, but most of the guys I knew had come because they'd been tossed out of home for being gay, or they couldn't live freely in their home towns. Homosexuality created a lot of expatriates. It still does, I would imagine. Also, when one is leaving Keokuk, an exit line like "I'm going to live in Manhattan" has a nice ring to it.

And there we were in ol' Lil's Beekman Place apartment sucking up her gin. We were in Manhattan with that view of the

Queensboro Bridge that MGM used as the backdrop for every apartment where the rich lived.

It was I who introduced Wesley into Lil's circle.

I had another reason for going besides Lil and her gin. I went because I had a crush on Teddy. I worshipped from a distance. Teddy was ferociously guarded by Robert.

Oh, you'll hear a good deal about Teddy, because we all loved him. Mostly, I suppose, because Teddy belonged to himself, in ways we didn't quite understand but probably envied.

But Teddy wasn't his own man because he'd chosen to be; he'd had to become so.

It might help you understand if you could see him. Go in the bedroom, and to the left of the mirror there's a picture of two people. One is me, the dazzler is Teddy.

He was one of the most beautiful men I've ever known: the open smile, the complete candor of the eyes, the very fair hair. He had it cut in the British fashion of the time . . . longer than American and combed in wings over the ears.

Teddy had created himself, that's why he belonged to himself. He came from somewhere in the Midwest. When he was in his teens his family found out he was gay. For a while they threatened to institutionalize him as insane. If they hadn't feared the scandal and gossip, they would have. So they let him remain at home, they just didn't speak to him. For over two years he was "sent to Coventry," as the British say. In his last year in high school he was beaten up by some men and nearly killed. He spent over two months in the hospital. No one came to see him. The day he was released from the hospital, he was handed an envelope by the nurse. It contained a Greyhound ticket to New York and twenty dollars. No note. None needed. He knew it was from his family. Not an altogether unfair amount in those days.

Teddy was always very funny about it. Mordant, but funny. As he used to say, when his family stopped talking to him he stopped hearing that he was inept, a sissy, and doomed to failure. Many adults complain that their parents ignored them, not realizing that they might have been spared a lot of punishment.

So Teddy had to create himself, make himself up, as it were. So he created a happy, charming man, and he always had a sure sense of what made him look attractive. It made him somewhat outrageous for those times, but it was right for him. He somehow perfected himself. Imagine being one's own Pygmalion.

Oh, you'll never get Robert or Billy to talk sanely about Teddy. Robert saw him as his chattel, and Billy saw him as his baby.

I loved Teddy, but I was much too inept to know what to do about it, except to be close to him as often as I could. If Teddy knew how I felt, he didn't let on and saved us both a good deal of embarrassment. We became good friends. Robert didn't much like that, I can tell you. But then, Robert didn't like anyone who was remotely close to Teddy.

Robert knows this, but I was partly responsible for Teddy's leaving him.

As I said, Teddy and I had become close, so when Billy came into his life and it got serious between them, Teddy came and talked to me about what was going on. He didn't tell me anything that wasn't pretty apparent.

Teddy loved Robert, but Robert insisted on being loved as he wanted to be loved, not as Teddy was able to love him. Robert wanted Teddy to shape up, butch up . . . to be "presentable," but by Robert's lights. He wanted Teddy to always be on hand, to be a convenience for Robert. Teddy took it for a long time. Longer than I would have.

Teddy didn't turn to Billy as a way out, he was an alternative.

I think Robert feared that if he lost Teddy there would never be anyone else, anyone else who would be as close. Robert could never accept that his feelings for Teddy were the result of Teddy's being who he was. Teddy's apparent docility and acquiescence were taken by Robert as feminine and weak. He loved Teddy, and disliked himself for wanting someone like that. If Robert had remade Teddy he would have hated the result.

I'm afraid that's all getting very Freudian. How can I make it clear? Well, for instance, there was that nasty bit of business over a new suit.

As I said, Robert hated the way Teddy dressed himself. Teddy made himself clothes that were bright and flamboyant and, I must say, absolutely right on him. And Robert hated every stitch of them, and called Teddy his "bird of paradise" in a most uncomplimentary tone.

So one day Robert dragged Teddy off to Brooks Brothers and

jammed Teddy into a navy-blue suit, white shirt, rep tie, the works. It was like spraying a parrot black. The effect was all wrong, and when Teddy wore that suit he had the pained expression of a woman in a tight corset.

The suit was "previewed" at Lily's, with Robert issuing instructions to Teddy on how one wore a suit: "Pull your trousers up when you sit down. A gentleman keeps his jacket buttoned when he's standing." It was awful. Finally, in an absolute fury, Robert screamed at Teddy, "You can't wear clothes like a gentleman. You never will. No matter what I do, you look like a streetwalker." Why Teddy took it I will never know. I'd have been murderous.

I think that's when Teddy started playing around. Robert was getting everything he said he didn't want. And a few weeks later Billy appeared on the scene. Teddy brought him to Lily's.

And it wasn't long after that Teddy decided to try making a life with Billy. That's when Teddy came to see me.

What it came down to was that Teddy didn't love Billy any more than he did Robert, but he guessed he could satisfy Billy by simply being Teddy. He knew he could never completely please Robert, because Robert was so disapproving of Robert.

Robert hated being gay. That's undoubtedly why he tried to go straight after Teddy left him.

I've been over all this with Robert. It comes up about every ten years . . . still.

I didn't say anything to Teddy, except that he should follow his own feelings in the matter. I think he did. And I must say, Billy was cute in those days. Billy was also tough in his own way.

Has Billy told you that Teddy was his baby? That's the way Billy saw it, but Baby had a mind of his own.

Teddy looked slightly frail, but he had strength. Teddy was never very sure about what he wanted to be, professionally, but he always knew who he was personally and made the best of it, or the most of it, or whatever term you care to use.

Robert also came to see me when he and Teddy were having a hard time of it. I don't think I've ever seen a man so broken up or so fearful. It was pitiable. I felt for him. I really did. But what could I do? I don't know what there was about Robert that made me feel any compassion for him. I hated the way he treated Teddy, I thought he was rigid and unfeeling. But I knew Teddy wouldn't get lost if he left Robert. I guess I sensed that Robert would.

I think I've been as close to Robert as anyone. Certainly as close as Robert will allow anyone to get.

And I must say that Robert's been very good to me, in his way. I'm very comfortable because of him. He helped me convert some of the stock I was living off into shares that have turned into bonanzas over the years. He's very good at that. After Price Waterhouse let him go, he turned that into a full-time business. Done very well at it. Done very well for me.

My career? All very spotty till Jack Warner picked me up, and here comes Lil again.

Lil used to put a little money into shows, mostly musicals. She started because it gave her access to a lot of rich people, potential clients. She also got to know the production people. She made good use of her contacts. A lot of the *mots* attributed to famous people of the time were hers. She didn't mind people using her wit. Like Elsa Maxwell, she felt her job was to make people around her look good. She was very shrewd not to try and hold center stage amongst that lot.

Lil started introducing me to theater people, and I got bits and pieces of work on shows . . . a little arranging here and there. But I'd never put myself forward. I was happy being the perennial student. I thought of my theater work as a diversion. I was almost surprised that I got paid for doing something I got such fun from. I thought I was doing well enough. I thought I lacked ambition. Lil understood me better than I did.

One night she asked me to dine with her alone. That was a rare honor. Over dinner she laid it on the line. She told me that everyone for whom I'd done work thought I was brilliant, but that all I ever did was come and get my instructions from the composer or whomever, go home, do the work, and deliver it like a messenger boy. She asked me straight out: "Are you really modest, or are you afraid they'll find out you're a cocksucker?"

I couldn't answer, because I started to tremble. She'd hit it. She had said what I hadn't even been able to think. It wasn't that I didn't trust my talent. I didn't trust others. What if they knew? Oh, that awful secret. When Lil said it, she brought all the fear up in me. I can remember sitting there wondering if I could keep from throwing up. Lil understood.

As she said, I could go on being "dynamite without a fuse," or I could have a wonderful career, anything I wanted. She'd thought it out.

She put it very clearly. She said that it was never content that counted as much as appearance. She said that the appearance of being straight was quite enough.

Lil told me that when she'd decided to have a go at being famous, she'd come into the city and spent over a year trying to pass. I'd never heard the expression "pass," and Lil explained that Negroes used it. If their skin were light enough they could pass themselves off as white and get into good jobs, hotels, restaurants, society.

She knew it was different for herself. She'd come into New York as Rose Mingus, awful accent and all, and worked her ass off to learn how to pass as high-toned, until she found that the qualities she'd tried to shed were what made her popular: the horse laugh, the dirty jokes, the Jewish wit. But it was different for me. I'd have to pass.

She said that my choice was not just whether I could be socially acceptable—to pass—but whether I ever wanted to really use my talent. She thought marriage would be wrong for me. She didn't think I had the temperament for any long-standing relationship, straight or gay. She was married to her career. She guessed I was married to mine. But she had a very good solution for me: debutantes.

Oh, Christ, here we go again. Another lesson on the period.

Well, ducks, debutantes were a kind of "royalty" in what was known as café society. The Depression hit the rich, too, but there were a few survivors and they got together with movie stars, deposed royalty, and gossip calumnists (you heard right), and some hangers-on, and they became known as café society. It was a very rigid social structure. But Lil said that room could always be made for a good-looking man on the way up. She said that the debs—before you ask, that's short for debutantes—didn't expect to be screwed, only danced with, usually till four A.M.

Lil proposed getting me in with that lot. Then I would "pass." Then I could stop worrying about whether people would find out about me.

Café society was a small world. There was a song at the time that began, "We are seen around New York,/El Morocco and the Stork,/And the other stay-up-late cafés . . ." That defined the enclave, the stamping grounds.

Lil guessed that the idea of using people like that might be appalling to me. It was. But she had a strong argument. As she said, I could go on schlepping my work around like one of the unwashed, or I could present a front that would get me what I wanted. If I wanted it. She wasn't sure that I wanted a career, but if being gay was what was holding me back, making me want to be invisible, then there was a solution. At the most, she said, I'd have to give my "cover work" two nights a week. And she had picked out the perfect deb for me to squire.

I thought about what Lily said for a whole week. What it came down to was very simple. If I wanted to exercise my talent, I was going to need a straight cover.

In a way, it's an awful cheat. It cheats everyone. It satisfies no one.

I'm wrong. I wasn't cheated. I got to work in my field, and to do work I loved and was good at.

I began my career as a gigolo with . . . what shall I call her? Let's call her Lucy Defarge. She looked like Dickens's Lucy Carton and acted like Madame Defarge.

Lucy was a marginal person. Marginally rich, marginally pretty, marginally intelligent. However, she was completely mean.

But Lily had chosen wisely, and Lily helped me budget the cost of escorting Lucy. Since Lucy could only afford her costuming, I was to pay for the public appearances. I needed Lucy, Lucy needed me. She was a bitch, but she liked me, and her meanness could actually be very funny.

She was what a friend of mine calls a "slight saver," and when she had a sufficient number of slights, she'd feed titbits about the offenders to columnists. So, after a while, people learned to tread lightly around Lucy.

Since Lucy and I worked the twelve-to-four shift at the clubs, I had to rearrange my work schedule. But I was young and had stamina, so it worked out all right.

Of course, everyone thought I was screwing the girl. Well, they were supposed to. The fact is, Lucy loved to talk about sex—other people's—but I think she was a virgin.

She eventually became a gossip columnist herself, and I can't think of a better preparation for being a gossip columnist than repressed sexuality and an overripe cherry.

But she seemed content with me, and some of it was really a lot of fun. Only some of it.

Most of it was boring. But those people had made it their job in life to have fun, so they stuck it out, night after night. They went through those evenings like mountain climbers roped together by necessity.

The Queen of the Debs, if you will, was a truly lovely young woman named Brenda Frazier. After I'd moved to the Coast, she sent me a poem she'd written, saying she hoped I'd be amused. She'd called the piece "Glamour Girl Serenade." I thought it was funny at the time, now I find it poignant. Let me read you some:

> I'm established now for 'thirty-eight
> With the title of glamour and reprobate.
> I've won a position in *Vogue* and *Harper's*;
> For a hundred bucks I'll advertise garters.
> I grit my teeth and smile at my enemies;
> I sit at the Stork Club and talk to nonentities.

Sad. But it does describe the deb.

But Lucy and I trudged on. Lily filled me with hope, and I filled Lucy with gin.

Finally, old Lucy paid off.

One of the rich lads in our circle was going to produce one of those socially-conscious musicals that cropped up from time to time in that period.

How can I disguise the project? Let's say it was a musical version of *The Lower Depths* set in contemporary Pittsburgh. I was invited to write the score.

I convinced them that a highly romantic score would lend an ironic color to the condition of the characters, and make the point that true beauty and honesty can only be found in the soul of the working poor. I figured that my bullshit was not a whit worse than the bullshit they were proposing to foist on the public.

The show repelled the public, but my score was lauded. One reviewer said that the score stood head and shoulders above the condescending pretensions of the book.

That's exactly what I intended. You see, I was learning.

That's when I got the call from Jack Warner. He was in town and wanted to hear the music from the show. Since the show had been stoned from the stage, he couldn't go to the theater and hear it. Just as well, because I was invited to his offices to play it for him.

I was awed by him from the moment we shook hands, and stayed awed for all the years I knew him. I have never seen such raw vitality in a man, not even in Cohn or Mayer.

When I'd finished playing, he said, "You Jewish?"

I said no, and he said, "Then you're smart as a Jew. You knew the show was shit, didn't you, but you got something out of it for yourself. They got *bupkus*. You got an agent? Good," he said. "You don't need one. I'll make you a fair offer."

There was a little more to it than that, but I left his office wanting very much to work for him, to work for Warner Brothers.

That was in 1936.

My affair with Wesley was on its last legs, so our good-byes weren't painful.

It's odd, but I can't remember missing anyone in New York. I'm afraid that music was still my whole life, and the idea of having a whole studio's music department to play with was thrilling.

No, I want to correct that. I missed Lily.

It's odd, but if I'd been looking for a mentor, I wouldn't have looked for a Lily. I'd have looked for a Stravinsky. But it was that tough, loving lady who made all the difference in my life.

Before I left, Lily and I tied one on and did a lot of crying. I don't remember it, but I apparently paid her one of her most cherished compliments that night. Apparently I told her that if I were straight, I would consider it an honor to fuck her.

When I arrived at Warners, all those plain cement buildings didn't put me off. The place looks like some kind of army testing center. Hardly a window anywhere, except the ones in the sets. But the recording stage was perfect, the best. We could get a sound that was the envy of the business. Our sound was richer and fuller than anyone's—even MGM's. And I was going to get to use it. My God, what a plaything for a musician.

Jack Warner started me on "programmers." They were what we turned out on a regular basis. They weren't the vehicles for top stars, but they had good budgets and they were paired to make good entertaining double bills. People got their two bits' worth.

I did about six of those programmers, back to back. My big break came when Steiner went off to work on *Gone With the Wind* and Selznick kept him longer than planned. I did the score for a movie they had him slated for. The movie was a hit, and my

score got a lot of good trade attention. Steiner was a "star" on
the lot, along with Korngold. But there were a lot of us, a lot of
other composers, all tops, all pros.

But that's all in my biography.

Gay life? I didn't see much of it. We were on six-day weeks,
often twelve-hour days. When I did get some time, it was usually
for a command performance at some producer's home, and I'd
have to squire some lady.

That's probably why when I met Jimmy I settled down.

I met Jimmy while I was helping on some of the prerecording
work on *Melody for Two*. It was a musical—one of our last for a
while—with Lawrence Tibbett and Lily Pons. Jimmy was a
singer in the chorus. Beautiful tenor, but he wasn't good enough
for the opera stage and he didn't have the looks for movies.

Jimmy lived with his mother. They had a small, sort-of-
Spanish house near the ocean. A little two-bedroom affair. He
looked after her. She drank.

There was nothing special about us. Jimmy was a couple of
years older than I—twenty-nine when I met him—and that must
have been about 1937.

Jimmy was long and thin, like an oboe, which often means a
bass or baritone voice, but he had this lovely tenor. A good solid
tenor, not reedy or shrill or like those awful tricky tenors who
always remind me of castratos when they do show-offy things,
shifting into falsetto. It's not singing. Jimmy wasn't a tricky
singer. Not good enough for opera, mind you, but splendid for
the kind of music we used in movies.

He worked a lot, was constantly on call from every studio in
town. He was a top tenor, and despite what you hear about the
studios they knew the best and used it.

Jimmy and I just seemed to work together. We admired one
another, we both loved music, and we were happy for whatever
time we could have together. It wasn't a lot. And we both loved
movies, and thought we were the luckiest people in the world to
be working in them.

Do you ever think of times in your life as enchanted? Those
years were. I didn't even know there was a war coming until the
studio made *Sergeant York*. Like a lot of my life in those days, I
found out what was going on in the world because of what the
studio decided to make.

Yes, it was an insular life, but if one never has some spaces in
their life like that, I pity them.

* * *

I'd get back East from time to time, usually on assignment to see Broadway musicals and scout talent for the music department, and I'd get to see my old chums.

By then, Billy was becoming a top man in decorating, but that's when his trouble with Teddy began. I didn't envy either of them. Old Wesley was constantly coming up trumps, one good role after another. All second-banana stuff, but solid. In '37 RKO signed him, and he became my neighbor out in L.A.

Something happened to Robert in the late thirties. He got himself into something terrible. He'll tell you, if he wants. Wesley and Billy and I got together and tried to help. We were some help, I guess.

And there was always Lily, and Lily was always Lily. Never changed. She even came out to the Coast for a while and stayed with me. Redid my whole house for me. I say redid, but when she arrived, about all I had was the beautiful Steinway I still have and two beds. One bed I'd bought for her arrival. She made the place handsome and beautiful, and hired a woman to clean for me who stayed with me all her life.

Yes, young man, I got quite rich. A lot of that's to Robert's credit. Billy did quite well, too. Wesley never did have any sense about money.

# Billy Hicks

Lily saved my tail. Don't forget, when I met her I'd been bounced out of college and out of General Electric. I didn't have a sou and I was living in the Y. I was nineteen. It's a ghastly thought, but now I could be the grandfather of someone nineteen.

Well, lovely Lily gave me a job. I don't think she really needed me, but I made myself useful. I wasn't dumb. Actually, I was a smart kid.

Teddy and I found a place in the Village—a wonderful little maze of a place, with tiny rooms—a doll's house. We put all we earned into it and made it quite enchanting.

I have no extraordinary things to say of those years. They passed. We were young and—how did someone put it?—life seemed to live us.

As for my sex life, there was just Teddy and me. We didn't play around. We never had any need to. And I loved looking after him.

A lot of gay people underestimate the advantages of being gay. There we were, two men . . . both earning money, no children, time to give to our careers.

I found I loved my work. And in the summer there was the place at Cherry Grove, just a shack, actually, but fine for lazy summers, and in those days Cherry Grove seemed very remote. It was remote then. Our lovely shack blew away in that hurricane in '38.

It was '37 before anything worth noting happened.

That's when I got my break. Actually, I made the break.

A furniture importer I dealt with told me about some furniture that he still had in his warehouse. It had been sent over in 1929 for a show in Chicago. Some Chicago group was going to have a show of furniture designed by architects, but when the Depression hit, they canceled the show, the importer wouldn't pay the freight back to Europe, and the people over there weren't willing to pay it, either. So there the stuff sat for eight years. He showed me the bills of lading, and I got very excited.

The names on those bills didn't mean much to many people in those days, but for me they were names of architectural gods of the Twenties: Corbusier, Mies, Breuer, and Gropius. It was their furniture in the crates. My friend wanted to know if I had any interest in it.

Did I!

Teddy and I had some savings, so I made the importer an offer on the spot and he accepted. I knew none of the furniture would fit in our apartment, but I couldn't let it go. I asked my friend to hold onto it a while longer, till I figured out what to do with it.

All that furniture was so different from what was being used in those days. The look of the thirties was streamlined, all aerodynamic curves and parallel chrome tubes and such.

The stuff I'd bought was good. Capital G, good. So good that it's still around, still sold. Most of it's over in the Museum of Modern Art.

I held onto it for about a year, until Lily got a client—a big man on Broadway—who said he wanted the townhouse he'd bought redone in a contemporary manner. Now, Lily was great with period rooms. She could do dazzling things with any period, but she knew nothing about modern—sorry, contemporary.

She did some sketches for the man and they were wrong. She didn't have an architectural sense of space. The man rejected her designs. I don't know where I got the nerve, but I asked her to let me try and design the job.

Well, my designs went over like a million dollars. Lily said, "I don't understand them. They look so icy, so empty." And I told her, "They're architectural."

So I did the job. I designed the first truly architectural interiors, years before Hans Knoll. The man's house made almost all the major design magazines of the time. Lily got the credit. But that was all right, because it brought her commissions for more of the same, and she let me do those jobs. Her business doubled that year.

A year later, Lily made me her associate. At twenty-three, I was associate to the top interior designer in New York.

Not bad for a cocksucker from Schenectady.

Lily was something of a showman, so she created a pedigree for me that was more appropriate than being the son of a factory worker. I was now a child of Hawaii who had trained in California. Both places seemed so remote in those days that we figured there was no way to check my story.

Well, I was launched, and I was asked everywhere.

I hate to admit it, but Teddy was a problem. In my own way, I was becoming something of a public figure and loving it, but in those days one didn't go everywhere with one's lover. Actually, hardly anywhere. Couldn't.

No, I didn't have to hide being gay, as long as people didn't think I did anything about it.

Lily told me never to make any bones about being gay. As she said, "Give 'em a little oo-la-la, honey. Nobody expects you to be butch in this business." But taking a lover around with one— never!

I'm not proud of this, but the only solution I could find to having Teddy around as a regular part of my life was to make him my assistant. That is, I had to tell people he was. I told most people he was my secretary.

Naturally, Teddy and I talked it over. It was terrible for both of us, and I did what I could to make it up to him. But my life changed. First, we moved to the apartment on Park Avenue, and finally to this house.

But I wasn't the only prominent man who had to fob his lover off as an employee. Not by a long shot. It's still being done.

I had to ask Teddy to stop doing sewing for Lily, and I really tried to give him some responsibility. But he had no feeling for the work, and when I tried to get him interested in designing, he didn't seem to care. I even tried sending him to school for a while.

It wasn't an easy time for us. I was out and away more and more often. Teddy started drinking a little too much, and I couldn't ask him not to. I mean, what else did he have.

Lil did what she could. She took him places with her, when I couldn't. And I gave him a good allowance and urged him to see our friends, to take them to lunch, let him handle all the household management.

But we came out of it all right . . . a lot better than some.

# Robert Regal

Teddy was a goddamned servant, that's what he was. Billy shoved him out of sight, because he'd become an inconvenience.

Teddy used to come here and cry his eyes out. I told him he shouldn't stay with Billy. It was doing terrible things to him. That's when his drinking started.

Billy tried to buy him off. Billy started making big money— very big for those days. And he'd buy Teddy clothes and jewelry. He decked Teddy out like a Christmas tree, but Teddy had almost nothing to do. Billy said that he wanted Teddy to have the best clothes, but what he really wanted was for Teddy to stop wearing those clothes he made for himself.

I don't know why Teddy stayed. I told him: Come here. You know you're welcome here. Get out of there.

My work was all right. It could have been better, but it was okay. Price Waterhouse didn't make managers in carload lots in those days, not the way they do now. But, still . . . still, I'd put in my time, done well for them. I wanted to be a manager with them. I didn't.

Of course nothing was ever said, and I wasn't about to ask why I didn't get my manager's contract.

I couldn't complain. In the thirties you held onto what you had.

Yes, I think there was some talk in the office. Jesus, you'd think the way people talk we'd chosen to be this way. Believe me, I would have changed.

I tried to change.

What fool would choose to be gay.

I took every cent I had and tried.

You kids just do what you want, and to hell with everyone else. It wasn't that way in my time. I keep telling you that.

I was stuck. You don't stay unmarried in a firm like that forever and make any progress. It made good sense to try, to try and go straight. I'm not ashamed of that. I wanted to feel like everyone else. Jesus, what life was there in the streets—all those casual affairs, never knowing anyone's name, just sneaking off after it's done and promising yourself you'll never do it again.

Who wouldn't want to change.

I didn't know where to begin to look for help. I was ashamed of myself for even looking. In those days, seeing a psychiatrist was the same as admitting you were crazy.

But at the library, I started reading the psychiatric journals. I was even ashamed to ask the girl for the journals. I was sure she'd know what I was looking for.

I found some articles by men who claimed they could cure it. I took all my money and went to one of them.

For the first two months I couldn't even bring myself to tell the man—the doctor, that is—that I was homosexual. But that's why I was there. I'd picked him because I'd read his piece in a journal on the use of a drug. It was called Metrazol. His article said he cured people like me with it.

How did Metrazol work? It produced *grand mal*.

The worst seizures epileptics have are called *grand mal*. That's what the drug produced, *grand mal* seizures.

I suppose it was horrible, but it wasn't any more horrible than what I had in life, shut up in my room, afraid for my job.

I couldn't go out of my room. I didn't want to. I couldn't be one of those awful people who haunt the streets. I only wanted what everybody had. And I wanted to get ahead.

It took all my savings, and I ended up in debt to him.

I had fifteen treatments in eight months. We went as fast as we could.

While it was going on—when I felt well enough—I dated a woman in the office. You see, I had hope. He told me that if I was willing to make any sacrifice, accept any hardship, I could be cured.

I could only have the treatments on Friday, because they left me so sick that it was days till I felt even so-so. My work suffered. But I thought I could do even better afterward . . . make it up.

That doctor was the one who urged me to take the woman to bed.

I have never been so ashamed in my life. It's humiliating to be told by a woman that she "understands." What the hell was it she thought she understood?

I thought, Yeah, honey. You'll be understanding till you get to the office and you get talking to your girl friends. And she certainly didn't have the best reputation around that place.

It was all a flop. A big, expensive flop.

Wesley finally wormed the story out of me. I guess they were really worried about me. After all that failed, I felt worse off than before. There'd been that small hope, and afterward, none. None left. I was hopeless.

Has Wesley mentioned any of this to you?

Small wonder.

# Wesley Ober

How I loved the thirties. I did a run of good shows on Broadway, did shots on *Pepper Young's Family* and *Ma Perkins,* and a lot of other radio shows, and got signed by RKO in '37, where I did almost no work and spent most of my time on loanout. They hired me at $750 a week and would loan me out to another studio for $1,500.

I'd spent some time on the Coast before, doing mostly westerns at the old Fox studios. Died in John Wayne's arms in one. You know the line: "Y'all look after Kate and Maw." Neck goes limp, head lolls, eyes close. Fade.

When I went back out there I was used as a Ralph Bellamy type.

Bellamy had a corner on "second man" parts, and he was also at RKO, which is why I spent so much time off that lot. Bellamy did all those roles where the woman, after hectic years with a Cary Grant type, decides she'll marry a stable, dull, boring man with money, only to find she still loves her first husband—mad though he may be. That kind of thing. I could do my parts in my sleep, and when critics said I did, they were right.

Just to show you the difference, Bellamy got to play with Irene Dunne, I got to play with Laraine Day. But I was a sound utility man. I never had Larry's drive or Cary's passion for success. Why ruin a lovely game.

I didn't miss New York at all. I loved the Coast when I was there. I love New York while I'm here, Capri while I'm there, London while I'm there. I seem to like where I am.

I had three weeks between pictures in 1938, and I came back East, mostly because Carl was coming and we could take the Chief together. The trip meant four days on a train, and I always liked company. Few people flew in those days, and certainly not coast to coast. I read *Gone With the Wind* that trip. I was up for a part, but Billy Stelling got it.

The trip gave Carl and me lots of time to catch up. We'd both had several letters from Teddy around this time, saying how worried he was about Robert.

Teddy said that something awful had happened to Robert. He said that Robert looked physically debilitated and couldn't seem to eat or concentrate. Teddy was afraid Robert might lose his job if things went on the way they were going.

Teddy and Robert had stayed friends, which always surprised us. In some ways, Robert was more Teddy's confidant than even Billy, certainly more so than Carl or me.

We knew that Robert was terrified that someone would find out he was homosexual. Teddy wrote that he thought Robert was ill, but I thought he might be being blackmailed. I thought that might be why he never spent any money and stayed in that grubby room of his on the West Side. Robert never seemed to do anything but work.

Anyway, Teddy asked us to help, so, of course, we said we would, but we didn't have any idea how or even what we were helping with. Robert often resented us. We didn't think he'd welcome any help, much less advice.

It was Lily who finally came up with an idea.

She didn't much like Robert, but she sized his position up better than any of us could have. "He doesn't have the chance of a snowball in hell of making it in that outfit he's with," she said. "If he's any good, they'll let him stay around, but he'll never get anywhere. He'd better start looking to go elsewhere, or, better yet, set up shop on his own." As usual, Lil was right. So, she suggested that Carl, Billy, and I each put up $5,000 and give it to Robert to manage for us . . . to act as a kind of broker. If it seemed to work, we would each increase our contribution every year and just see what happened. That was a lot of money in those days, but we had it.

As I said, Lily didn't like Robert much—not a bit, to be frank—but she thought he was smart and well informed. As she said, all he ever did was sit up in that room of his and read. In the end, she added her own five thousand.

I've no idea why we thought Tony's would be a good place to meet and discuss our proposal, but we dragooned Robert to Tony's one night.

We all loved Tony's, but it was the kind of place that put

Robert off. It was swanky. Tony's was where what we called the "smart charts" went. And we were. We were all young and good-looking. We were much too grand for the Village, and at Tony's you could see Lillie and Bankhead and Hayes, and lots of famous people. And we all had a little fame by then, too.

That's where we took Robert to make our proposal to him. We must have thought he'd be grateful for our offer, give us a hug, and we would all get high and celebrate. We were wrong.

Robert just sat glowering. Here he was in a den of homosexuals. As usual, the place was jammed, and the crowd was always pretty to look at, very animated, and a little noisy. Robert got the evening off to a good start by saying that he'd never seen so many Nancy swishes in his life. We loved the place. We felt at home there, so we didn't take the remark too kindly. Robert also made some rude comment about the women the boys brought along as covers.

Lil was with us. She didn't take that too well, and she told him so.

Then Billy, who was always edgy with Robert, looked very angry and started to say something, but Teddy got in first and said, "Robert, I'm one of those Nancy swishes. That didn't seem to bother you in bed." Nobody but Teddy could have said that to him.

Robert cooled off, and we had a couple of rounds. We were pretty uncomfortable, and nobody seemed to want to talk about what we'd come there for. Once Billy leaned over to me and said, "Fuck the whole idea."

You'd wonder why we had anything to do with Robert. In a way, it's hard to remember. Let me see if I can help you understand.

Well, for one thing, Robert could talk to me alone, or he could talk to Carl alone, and be very pleasant, very nice to each of us. But he couldn't handle more than one person at a time, and gay groups in public made him panic. Alone he'd do anything you asked him. More than anything, I guess, it was Teddy who kept him near us, asked us to care for him. Teddy saw something we didn't, I suppose. We all adored Teddy, and Teddy needed Robert.

It's hard to see now, he looks so . . . so different, but Robert was very good-looking then. He could have had anything he wanted, anybody in Tony's, and they were the pick. But he wouldn't even have had Teddy for a while, if Teddy hadn't made the first move. It was sad, but Robert completely wiped out any personality he might have had by acting what he imagined to be "straight." It just made him seem rigid, what you kids call "uptight." It showed in his face, the way he stood, everything. He looked formidable.

Anyway, after Robert had put a damper on things, we just sat and looked at one another for a while.

It was Teddy who got things back on the track. I remember it pretty clearly, because it was unlike Teddy, but he said to Robert, "You can be such a dumb shit. The only reason we're all here is because they thought they might help you get started toward having a business of your own." Teddy told him we were willing to put up five thousand each and let him get us into the stock market. He'd be our broker. Teddy went on at Robert for being so mean-minded when people wanted to be his friends. And I'll never forget the last of it. Teddy said, "Robert, do you know how hard people work at caring about you? Please, for a change, let them."

Robert just sat looking at Teddy, thinking God knows what. It was pretty dim in there, but I could see that Robert was crying. He had to leave the table. Teddy went after him. We took his crying for gratitude.

Seeing Robert cry was not an easy thing to watch. It seemed to tear his face apart. I think we took that as some kind of breakthrough with Robert, and we all felt very good about ourselves finally getting through to him.

Robert did become our broker and we did well, and in a few years he had his own business.

None of us knew for a long time that Robert had put himself through that chemical thing with the doctor. He'd certainly never told us. Teddy was the one who told us he'd almost died from one of the treatments and had to be hospitalized for three weeks. Knowing Robert, that must have been terrible for him, because the hospital had to know why he'd been given that drug. And that's about the time that company he worked for let him go. Oh, he got another job, but it was in some awful place way the hell and gone in the Bronx. Working for that classy outfit in Wall Street had meant a lot to him. I think it helped him feel good about himself.

I wonder what would have happened to him without Teddy. Teddy's the one who got Robert out of that awful room and into that apartment he still has. Look around his place; everything

Teddy put there is still in place. It all needs a good wash, but it's still there.

As Lily predicted, Robert did very well with our money. You see, Robert was the only one among us who saw war coming, so he bought us things like Du Pont and Lockheed and Sikorsky and RCA, and that kind of thing in the thirties when the stocks were still depressed.

I certainly didn't know a war was coming, even in 1940, because I pulled my money out of the stocks and bought a beautiful black Lincoln Continental and drove a lovely young man from MGM off for a month in Mexico.

Robert's absolutely right about me: I never had any sense about money, that's why I don't have any now. I'd be rich now if I'd followed through on that deal we set up. But I'm silly about money. In the early forties I owned a big spread in Beverly Hills. Sold it. As my dad used to say, "If wishes were horses . . ."

Although I was on the Coast, I knew a great deal about what was happening back here, because Teddy had a lot of time on his hands and would write me long letters. Long distance calls were still a little special. I still prefer letters; they say more, they have personality.

Oh, I knew Teddy was drinking too much. Teddy told me. He didn't like what it did to him, but he had all that time on his hands, and we all thought it would pass, was just a phase.

I want to give you a letter from Teddy. I'll leave it up to you whether to use it. You can decide when you're putting the book together. But it fills in some of the spaces.

By the way, we'll have to cancel next week's session. I have to go into the hospital for some tests. No, nothing serious, but as David says, at my age something is always falling off or out.

David who? David Niven.


[The following is excerpted from a letter Teddy sent Wesley Ober. I can only ask Billy Hicks to forgive me if it troubles him, but it sheds light on some matters. Also, in its way, it is a testament of love.—C.N.]


                                               March 7, 1938

Dear Wesley:
    How's the shooting on *Speed to Burn* going? If it's one of those auto-racing movies, I won't go and see it even if you are in it. I can't stand all that noise.

When are you coming back East? Do come back, and soon. I could use a laugh and a little fun.

I've just come back from Robert's and he looks like death. For a while I dreaded cancer, but he says it's not that. But he is seeing a doctor for something else. But he won't say what for.

I've got to tell someone, so it might as well be you. Robert and I are sleeping together again. I don't know whether it started because I felt sorry for him or sorry for me or he felt sorry for me. One day I started crying and he held me and we ended up in bed.

Billy's a big item these days (Schiaparelli opening last night, a Broadway opening tonight), and I've written you what my days have become. (I'm a rotten shopper.) Billy's out early and home late. Do I sound like Helen Trent? And I'm not thirty, either. (No cracks.)

Well, since I've started, I may as well tell you the whole thing. I'm also spending some of my afternoons at the Everard Baths, and when I'm not there I'm in Tony's trying to pick someone up. And I'd go to the subway johns, if I weren't afraid of getting arrested.

I can't jump on Billy about this. He's hitting his stride and it's good for him. It's just not good for *us*. He's ambitious, and I never knew that. I guess I thought we'd just stay here on Carmine Street forever, but Billy's got plans.

I don't doubt he loves me. I know he does. But I don't fit, I don't work, and I feel useless, and so I screw around a lot.

I'm not asking you what to do. I just had to get it off my chest to someone. You're far away and I trust you. (I trust you close, too, honey.)

I guess all I can do is hang around. Maybe it's not all as "Kay Francis" as I make out. Maybe I'm making too much of the whole thing.

Anyway, I couldn't just solve my problem by running off. I love Billy, Wesley.

Well, finish your silver-screen epic and come back so I can cry all over you.

Love to you and the other stars,
TEDDY

# PART 5

# Drum and Bugle Music
## The Early Forties

The four men in this book all did wartime jobs during the Second World War. Any of them might have avoided service by proclaiming their homosexuality. It doesn't seem to have even occurred to them: They just assumed it was their responsibility to serve on behalf of their beleaguered country.

It is not likely that today's gays would march off so unquestioningly. They might well ask, "Why should I fight for a country in which I have no constitutional rights, am illegal, am punitively taxed, am denied work, and fired for my sexuality."

If gays hadn't gone into service, the U.S. Army of the Second World War might have been at least ten percent smaller, because our apparently single state disqualifies us for deferments based on marriage or most other "compassionate" reasons.

But off the gays marched, sometimes with both halves of a gay couple going into one service or another, to risk not only life, but also the discovery of their sexual secret, a discovery that could bring court-martial and dishonorable discharge. And dishonorable discharge could brand a man for life, forever damaging his ability to work to the full limits of his talents and earning capacity. For gays, entry into the armed services carried a double jeopardy: the wounds of war, the damage of discovery.

Even if a gay's sexual secret remained hidden from the upper echelons of the service, discovery by others close to him could turn his service time into hell. Harassment of gays is unofficially sanctioned and seems to be harshest in the services where, statistically, there is a larger percentage of gays than in civilian life. That statistical quirk remains a paradox in service life to this day.

Perhaps the significant difference between World War II and more recent conflicts such as Vietnam is that the issues seemed so clear-cut and uncontroversial back then. Movies of the period, which seem so jingoistic to today's audiences, were generally accepted at face value, since they reflected the consensus. In those films, the enemies are monstrous demons and Americans are the defenders of all that is virtuous, honest, humane, and civilized. Most certainly, the Japanese attack on America's base at Pearl Harbor, Hawaii, was an unambiguous message from the Japanese that read, "We're going to destroy you."

At the time of which our four subjects speak in this section (from late 1941 on), the British, with whom we Americans felt our greatest international kinship, had lived on the brink of annihilation for over two years. Nazi Germany was allied to Japan, and Italy completed the aggressive triumvirate known as the Axis. It was this triumvirate against which America declared war within days after the attack on Pearl Harbor.

By the time of the Japanese attack on America, almost all of Europe was under Nazi control and the Germans had seized a vast tract of Russia. In the East, Japan was entrenched throughout Asia and within striking distance of Australia. For a long time America successfully ignored these realities. So the Japanese attack was, for most, an immense surprise, and in retrospect seems almost like a desperate attempt by Japan to get the U.S. to come out and fight. We were jolted awake, and for the first time realized that the oceans that embraced our shores had turned to lakes.

To put the world situation of that time simplistically, the Axis Powers were the bad guys, the Allies were the good. And there were few who questioned that. There were few Americans who didn't do their "duty" and do it without any reference to their personal situations.

Any effort to encapsulate an entire war is doomed to failure, but I feel that some sense of the magnitude of that war is needed to set a stage for Wesley, Carl, Billy, and Robert, no matter how skimpily it might be furnished, no matter how dim the light. So it is to a degree an admission of my helplessness at the task that I fall back on a random collection of statistics, but they do offer some scant idea of the magnitude of a war that engaged almost every person on the planet.

- In the Pacific war the Allies were in almost continuous rout until late 1942 when, by leapfrogging from one

Pacific scrap of island to another (Iwo Jima, Okinawa, Eniwetok, Guadalcanal—more than a hundred in all), the Allies were able to form a noose that tightened around Japan. This strategy was pursued at immense cost. For instance, at Iwo Jima alone casualties were at least fifty percent.

• Because of submarine action, not all American bombers and airmen reached Europe (both went by ship), but of those that did, 18,500 bombers and 64,000 airmen were shot down.

• By May, 1944, two and a half years after the outbreak of war, about 2.8 million men—mostly American—were gathered in England with sufficient weaponry to launch D Day.

• In 1939 only two percent of America's productive output was in munitions, but by 1944 our assembly lines were spewing out fifty percent more armaments than the Axis nations combined.

• In about five years, American war production produced almost 300,000 aircraft, over 71,000 naval ships, 41.5 billion rounds of ammunition, and vast quantities of all other manner of war matériel.

The kind of world in which that war took place was a world in which a transatlantic phone call was a prerogative of statesmen, a world without transatlantic flight (it still took five days sea travel), without television, a world that was precomputer, pre-electronics, before radar, sonar, satellites, miracle drugs, or plasma. Man still moved himself and his communications at speeds and in quantities that were only fractions of what we know today.

Almost nothing is adequate to convey the difference between that physical world and today's, to convey a sense of that war which in its own rudimentary way would devastate millions, to convey that cast of thought that made Americans enter war without question, as our four speakers did.

This next section offers a look at some gays at war. While it doesn't presume to speak for gays at large, it does offer some insight into how our covert sexuality can add immense burdens beyond those felt by the majority of Americans living similar war-disrupted lives.

# PART 6

## "Let's Remember Pearl Harbor"*

*First propaganda song to achieve national popularity during World War II.

# Carl Mason

I think Warners was the first to make a war movie, if you can count *Confessions of a Nazi Spy*. Considering the times, I don't know what possessed the studio to produce *The Fighting 69th* and *Sergeant York*, but they both did very well. I was surprised. I hated war movies and I couldn't imagine anyone paying money to see them.

If I was aware of what was going on at all, it was because we started getting so many job applications from foreign musicians. I don't know how they found their way to Hollywood, but they seemed to be coming from all over Europe. I auditioned some of them, but I don't remember hiring any until after the war started and some of our younger studio musicians signed up or got drafted.

No, I never talked to any of them about what was happening, why they'd come to America. I think I assumed they'd come because it was a great place to be. I listened to a lot of talent. Some of them were stars with the orchestras they'd played with abroad, and I was just overjoyed to hear their wonderful music. Some of them were brilliant, and I would have loved to have hired them. Some I did, eventually.

As I've said, I never had much time for anything but music, and we worked very long days and long weeks at the studio. Don't forget, we turned out over one feature movie every two weeks, to say nothing of two-reelers, trailers, and cartoons.

I didn't know there was a war coming, I just knew there were a lot of foreign musicians around.

Of course I remember where I was when the Japs bombed Pearl Harbor, just as younger people remember where you were when Kennedy was assassinated, or Martin Luther King.

However, I must admit that I didn't understand what had happened.

I remember it was a Sunday and that I was working on a sound stage with the orchestra. I'm not sure whether I was recording the music track because a production was late or because of that crazy California law that taxed unreleased movies.

I remember the moment, because something sacrilegious happened: The fellow who manned the desk outside the stage came into the room in the middle of a take and ruined it. It was his job to keep people out if the red light was on outside the door, so I was furious when I heard the door and saw him tiptoeing toward me. I remembered I yelled at him. "There's no use tiptoeing now, goddammit, you've ruined a take." But in he came, and he came over to me and whispered in my ear, "The Japanese have bombed Pearl Harbor." And I whispered back, "I don't give a damn if they've bombed Santa Monica Boulevard. You get your ass out of here and fast." I must have scared him, because he ran out and I just tapped my baton and got back to work. I didn't tell the orchestra.

We had to rewind the film and go back a whole scene. If I remember rightly, the scene we were working on had Alexis Smith in it.

The news didn't make any impression on me, because I had no idea where Pearl Harbor was or what it was. My lover Jimmy explained it to me that night, and I still had trouble understanding why everyone was so excited and upset about someplace way off in the Pacific. Hawaii wasn't even a state then. It always surprised me that Jimmy seemed to know so much about so many things.

I remember that Sunday evening well, not so much because of Pearl Harbor, but because Sunday was when I always went to Jimmy's for supper, and his mother made it more than usually awful that night.

Those Sunday evening dinners were always a trial. Jimmy's mother hated me. She knew what was going on between Jimmy and me. She said it was the reason she drank. I tried to get him to move out, but the few times he'd tried moving out on her, she'd fallen to the floor gripping her heart and moaning. So Jimmy stayed. He was too sweet for his own good.

I'd tell him, "Move out and we'll send her a case of gin a week for life. Then she won't have to steal from the grocery money."

I remember the night well, because Mum got more than usually drunk.

They lived near the ocean, and the deck of the house looked out on the Pacific. It was a beautiful setting, actually, but it was a dark house, the way California houses can be. All small windows. They move to the Coast and then build houses to keep out the sun.

I remember the house as very Nita Naldi, all Spanish shawls and beadwork lampshades and plaster nymphs on tiptoe. Awful joint.

As usual, Jimmy cooked dinner and Mum sat slopped in a chair with her glass, except that she kept hearing the Japs landing on the beach and would bolt from her chair and dash onto the deck screaming. It was unsettling.

We couldn't get her to eat. She thought we were unpatriotic for eating when America stood on the brink of annihilation, so she went back to her gin and Jimmy and I ate alone.

Jimmy talked about joining up that evening. I was furious with him. I said, "You won't leave that old bitch to come and have some kind of life with me, but you'll go off to some silly war and get yourself killed." I told him, "If they want me, they're going to have to come and get me."

The best I could do that night was to get him to agree to wait and see what was going to happen. He scared me. I had my work and I had Jimmy, and when I realized that he might go away, I realized how much I loved him.

Foolish fucking war!

I made him come home with me that night. He didn't want to leave her alone, but by ten or so she was passed out. She wouldn't miss him. I made sure that the liquor cabinet was full, so she wouldn't wake up and start calling my place.

I took him home and we made love all night. I was very afraid of his going.

But I couldn't talk him out of it, couldn't talk him out of signing up. I just delayed him. He went in as a simple private. He took his lovely talent and his lovely person and went away.

I pleaded with him not to rush off, to hold on. The industry had a lot of power in those days. I might have been able to see that some proper use was made of that beautiful man. You won't remember, but the Army put together a show called *This Is the Army* using enlisted men. Irving Berlin wrote it. Jimmy would have been perfect for that. He went in while they were casting it.

We made a movie of the show at Warners and I did some work on it. I kept thinking: If Jimmy had done as I'd wanted, he'd be here now shooting the movie. It was a wonderful show, but I hated it because he wasn't in it.

You know what his mother said when he told her he'd signed up. She said, "I'm surprised they're taking sissies." But she hung the star in her window so everyone would know there was someone in her family in the service. They were sleazy rayon flags. Every blue star on the flag meant a family member in service. A gold star meant one of them was dead.

My God, why am I getting so worked up about all this. It was forty years ago.

My memories of the studio at that time are a blur. Everyone seemed to be rushing about. Jack Warner was terrified that he'd lose all his male stars. He didn't. Bogart and Cagney and Garfield and Flynn all stayed on to win the war single-handed— on film. . . .

Jimmy's voice is on the track of *Yankee Doodle Dandy* and I can pick him out. He comes through clear as a bell. That was the last thing he did at Warners. I've always wondered if it wasn't that jingoistic movie that didn't convince him to "do his duty," as they used to say. There was no stopping him.

Well, whatever. The fact is that after work on that track he left.

He was so frail-looking. I thought, Well, they won't take him. Just one look at him and you could see there wasn't much to him. Skin and bones. But he signed up for the infantry one afternoon and they took him.

I'd been able to keep him from signing up by getting him to promise me every morning that he wouldn't do anything that day. "Wait a couple of days. See how things go," I'd say. It wasn't as if he wasn't doing something useful. I said, "At least sign up to entertain. If you've got to get into this thing, contribute what you can do best."

He felt that would have been cowardly. Maybe he had to prove himself, or prove his mother was wrong about him. Who knows?

It was only March, only a couple of months after Pearl, when he called me late and said he'd signed up. Just regular army, just infantry.

I don't know what I felt. I don't remember feeling anything. I could make something up, but I don't remember. I really don't.

I remember going to the train station—down to Union
Station—to see him off. We'd agreed I wouldn't, and I could see
the sense in that, in not going. Not going would hurt, but I could
see the sense. Besides, he'd told me his mother was going down
to see him off, and that would have made a bad situation
impossible.

But a little before his train was due to leave, Ray, one of our
friends, came into the studio to record some music with a chorus
and told me he'd called Jimmy to say good-bye and that Jimmy
was in tears. There'd been some awful scene with his mother.
She was drunk. Jimmy was going off alone, with no one there
to say good-bye.

It was the only unprofessional thing I've ever done, but I got
the first violinist to take over the recording session and I ran off
to Union Station.

The place was chaos. Trains ran for the war, not for civilians,
and if you were traveling, you just had to get to the station and
take your chances that you'd get on something. But they got the
servicemen out on time. They got them off.

Did you ever see Judy Garland in *The Clock*? There's a
harrowing scene where she tries to find her lover in a mass of
people only minutes before his train is due to pull out. I played
the scene before she did.

Thank God he was tall. I spotted him near a gate and shoved
my way through this awful mob that was going every which way,
carrying everything they owned, like refugees. I felt so choked
when I saw him. I couldn't even call to him.

Well, he turned and saw me and I knew I'd made an awful
mistake, because he just started to cry. He'd been talking to
some men standing near him, and he'd looked up, saw me, and
started to cry. And I knew I couldn't go near him, couldn't have
those men see that he was crying because he'd seen me, crying
because of me, crying for another man. They'd have known
about him, and they'd have made his life hell.

I took it all in in a second. All those young men—all our age—
holding girls, kissing them, missing them already, I suppose.
. But I couldn't go near Jimmy, because I could hurt him
terribly, really do him damage. What else could I do? I turned
away and got out of his sight as quickly as I could.

I felt awful for putting him in that position. I felt awful that I
couldn't hold him. But I was so glad I saw him.

* * *

All the studios were booming. We were given a priority for film stock, and if we could make a good case for it, we even got some color stock.

I scored bombers soaring and submarines diving and orchestrated enough variations on "America the Beautiful" and "Anchors Aweigh" to make a symphony.

Somehow or other, the studio had gotten me a deferment. I hadn't asked for it, but someone had arranged for me to be draft exempt on the grounds that I was essential to the studio, which was essential to the war effort. I didn't want it.

I didn't want anything at the time. It was the only time in my life when my music seemed trivial to me.

Jimmy wrote me and asked me to look in on his mother from time to time. He knew I didn't like her and, Christ knows, he knew she didn't like me. But for Jimmy, I did it.

I didn't give a damn about her. I looked after her because I couldn't stand being to blame if anything happened to her. Maybe I just wanted Jimmy to have some peace of mind about her. Whatever the reason, I did it.

I saw that she got her booze, I drove her to the grocery every now and then. But I stopped that. I finally hired a kid at the studio who lived near her to drive over once a week and do what needed doing. I'd had it with the old bitch when she wouldn't even share her letters from Jimmy.

That may sound like a trivial reason, but you see, Jimmy and I had to stop writing to one another. The letters had been bad enough, hard enough to write, full of the kind of crap one gets in letters from people who are almost strangers. We couldn't take a chance of saying anything personal. We didn't know whether mail got censored, or who might accidentally find a letter. Jimmy had no privacy.

The writing ended when the guys on Jimmy's base picked up on all the letters he was getting from me, to say nothing of the letters he wrote me every day. So we just stopped. It wasn't as bad as it sounds. Actually, I was relieved. Have you ever tried to write a letter that says everything but what's on your mind? I'd bottled all those feelings up and they hurt. I imagine it was the same for Jimmy.

He'd call occasionally. He couldn't from the base, and he never knew when he'd get to a phone with some privacy. We were cut off. And phones are unsatisfying and frustrating, and all I'd do when he called was cry. What a mess. What an awful mess.

God! Now that I think about it, I spent most of those early months awash in tears. And the music was no good, it was no help. For the first time in my life, I couldn't concentrate. I did my work by rote.

For some reason, I took to wandering over to sit by the tank. Warners had built a huge water tank for staging sea epics, and it had just been finished when the war started. That probably accounts for the fact that Warners made more naval dramas than any of the other studios. Everybody went to sea at Warners.

I'd wander over to the tank almost every day and just sit and stare at it, and if there wasn't anyone around I'd have a good cry.

Everything had come loose. Everyone was scattering. By August everyone seemed to have found someplace to be useful except me. Billy was in Washington. That awful Pentagon was being built and he was designing generals' offices or some such. Wesley was a colonel. God knows how, but Wesley was a colonel. Robert was in the OPA [the Office of Price Administration]. Only Teddy and I were still civilians. I didn't know what to do, and Teddy said, flat out, that he wouldn't go. Oh, what an ungodly stink there was about that.

# Billy Hicks

I don't care what anyone else has to say in the matter, I still feel that Teddy did himself a great harm by not enlisting. But I'm not sure that any of this is worth going into. My God, no one even remembers that war, and judging by all I hear, war is very much out of style in our country.

It wasn't *infra dig* then. Not in 1941, not against Nazis or Japs. Going was the only thing a man could do. To be young and well and out of uniform was to be a pariah. Being out of uniform marked you as physically unfit—or worse. Everybody who could joined up, or tried to.

Lily and I had a lot of rich clients. We had nothing *but* rich clients, and most of them found a place in the war effort, even the older ones, even a lot of the women.

Lily and I saw the war coming, perhaps earlier than most. Lily's relatives started fleeing Europe in the early thirties, and now and then a gay German would show up in New York with improbable stories that nobody wanted to listen to. Dead Jews—even disappearing ones—were not the hottest topic of conversation. Besides, who could credit what we were hearing.

Lily and I noticed things in business. English wools just disappeared from the market. Orders for French and Italian fabrics would only get filled now and then, but you just couldn't depend on them, so we finally had to stop specifying them and work with what was at hand. You should have heard the outrage from our best customers. Wars were a nuisance, but not having a good French glazed chintz was absolutely un-American. Finally, we hired a nice old man who did nothing but scout fabrics for us, and if we found a few bolts anywhere we'd buy the lot and tuck it away. That's how Lily and I started Continental Fabrics.

I'll bet we bought up over half of anything worth having in the

99

late thirties. And we started doing business as suppliers when the war cut off everything from abroad. It was Lily who started getting American mills to produce better lines to take up the slack. She changed the whole fabric business in this country.

Yes, we knew something was going on, but everything was an ocean away. It was a lovely big ocean then. It was a nuisance in business, but not much more than that, certainly not enough to make us feel that the whole world would get turned upside down.

I suppose it's foolish of me to still feel so strongly about Teddy's not joining up. Nowadays, a lot of young gay men would do exactly what he did. But times are different now. In the world we lived in then, there was no question about what he should do.

Yes, I am reluctant to talk about what happened. Odd. Forty years later and it still upsets me, still churns me all up. I agreed to be frank, so here goes.

Teddy and I were at the Capitol. That was MGM's movie house on Broadway at Fifty-first Street. *Smilin' Through* was playing, and I'd go see anything with Jeanette MacDonald. Besides, it was her first movie in Technicolor. Perfectly awful, I suppose, but I loved it. They stopped the movie and the manager came on stage and announced that the Japanese had attacked Pearl Harbor. I remember that there was a great buzz in the audience and Teddy leaned over and whispered to me, "I hope Pearl isn't too upset." Not very funny, but it got to me and I started giggling and couldn't stop. I could've killed him.

I knew where Pearl Harbor was, because that was where Lily and I had been telling people I came from. (I went all through the war with people asking me what happened to my family at Pearl Harbor. I made up wonderful stories.)

I couldn't stop laughing, so Teddy and I had to get up and go into the lobby. What a gorgeous piece of *kitsch* that theater was. Teddy and I just stood in the lobby clutching one another and laughing, and getting a lot of dirty looks from people who were upset enough by the news to leave the theater.

When I pulled myself together, Teddy asked me what all the fuss was about. I told him that Pearl Harbor was a naval base and we'd been attacked by a foreign country. Even though Hawaii was "home," I only had a sketchy idea of what the attack meant. And I was a lot more interested in seeing how the movie ended.

When the movie ended and we left there wasn't a soul waiting to get in, and we'd waited in line a long time.

We stayed home that night, and everybody was calling everybody else, and wondering what it all meant and what would happen. I knew enough to know that it meant war and that I'd have to go.

Going to war didn't bother many of us, I suppose, because we really didn't know what going meant. It seemed the thing to do. There was a Dutch movie, a while back, and when the hero's country declared war, he said, "A spot of war might be fun." It was all so far away.

I said it to Teddy that night, "If we go to war, I'm going to join up." I also said a lot of very patriotic things I won't repeat, but I still feel pretty much the same way, and, given the same situation, I'd probably do the same thing.

When I thought about it later, I remembered that Teddy didn't say much . . . just sat and listened, and, judging by what happened, made his own decision that night.

I wasn't actually inducted until early February in '42, but by that time everything had changed. The whole world had changed.

When Teddy told me he wasn't going to join up, I was very angry with him. Furious, actually. The country needed everyone. If you read any history, you know that this country could well have gone under. We came *that* close.

I said it to Teddy at the time, so I suppose there's no reason not to say it to you. The army might well have been the best thing in the world for Teddy. I loved him—still do in many ways, still miss him—but I could see his shortcomings. My darling was epicene.

I did start to leave Teddy behind, but I didn't stop loving him, and I never stopped wanting him to have some life of his own.

None of this makes any sense unless I can make you see how much I loved that man. I cared enough for him not to be less than I could be. Even when I felt the strain. If I'd held my career back, I would have ended up hating him.

It wasn't a bad bargain for us. It was often a very good bargain.

Teddy can't speak for himself, but he loved me enough to stick it out. Whether our motives were good or bad, we lasted, and there is no use worrying over how it might have been better. The fact is, it might have been worse, or it might not have been at all.

But no matter how my motives may look in retrospect, they were always weighed in Teddy's favor, because I sensed it was easier for me to have less in our bargain.

Well, make what you will of it. Everyone else does.

Oh, God, how can I make this clear? I told him, "If the army will take you, it could give you a sense of purpose, help you gain some self-respect."

The way our lives were going, it didn't make any sense for him to go back to sewing all that crap for Lily, and he wasn't happy running our house, and he was even worse at assisting me. He was flailing about, and even the drinking wasn't a secret by then. His joining would have made great sense. Besides, I'd be going and there'd be even less of a life for him.

I don't understand. I still don't understand.

What he did and the way he did it was completely pointless. It's one of the few things in my life that I'm bitter about, that the war damaged Teddy in the most awful way. Not directly. No bomb on Fifth Avenue, but the war did it—ignominiously and pointlessly. I still blame Robert for encouraging Teddy in what he did.

My God, listen to me. After all these years, still angry about all that.

The day after the attack on Pearl, I called some clients who I knew had connections in Washington and told them I wanted to enlist. I asked them to do some asking around and see if they couldn't find something useful for me to do. There was no sense in rushing off to some recruiting station like some rube. I wanted to serve, but I wanted it to be something useful, something I'd be good at.

When I got home that night, Teddy was still out. He came in very late, said he'd been at Robert's. I told him that I'd started asking around about finding a spot for myself in one of the services. I admit it, I was fired up by the whole thing. Perhaps too much so.

Teddy listened to me, and then told me that when he got his notice to appear for induction, he planned to tell them he was homosexual.

I remember his arguments. We went over the same ground every day until I left. Teddy said that everything he'd ever wanted to do was denied him, because he looked like what he was. He kept saying, "I look like a fag, because I am a fag." He said he could do well enough around his own kind, but, heaven knows, even a lot of them avoided him. He told me that he was afraid that even if he managed to get into the army, he'd be killed. He wasn't afraid of being killed by some enemy, he was afraid that the other men would kill him.

Telling the induction people he was gay was just an act of useless defiance. I never relented, but I told him that if he was determined on staying out, there were other ways. We were already hearing about pills that would produce a temporary heart murmur.

Teddy went and told the induction people he was gay. He said they handled him with tongs after he told them. They gave him a draft card that said he was 4-F.

Four-F was—well, it was what you call a put-down. Saying someone was "a 4-F" was almost like saying he was a coward. You couldn't get a job without a draft card, and people were not at all shy about asking why you weren't in service. Teddy's 4-F card moved him even farther out of society.

I can see that you don't understand what it meant to be 4-F at that time. Today you're a hero if you burn your draft card, today you're applauded, and you run off to Canada, or wherever.

I'm talking about 1941. I'm talking about a war that made sense to everyone. Teddy's choice made him a pariah, and I spent a lot of time defending him, defending his choice, and I hated what he'd done. I'm still not glad he did what he did.

Outside of Teddy, not one of my gay friends didn't serve in some way. And there was a lot of resentment against Teddy for doing what he did. Not serving was like disowning your country. That's what Teddy wanted to do—disown his country. He told me so, that's how I know. They'd never wanted him, now he didn't want them—or their "goddamned war," as he put it.

# Robert Regal

Of course I knew there was a war coming. You'd have had to be blind or illiterate not to have seen it coming.

The *Times* even sounded alarmed. I was home reading the paper when the news about Pearl Harbor came over the radio. They interrupted the Philharmonic concert with Rodzinski and Rubinstein. Shostakovitch's First. All I could think was "finally." They've finally done it.

I was working for that awful company up in the Bronx and they imported this and that, odds and ends. But mostly sugar. Also, I remember that we couldn't get tapioca. There was a tapioca shortage. It came from the Far East and it just couldn't be gotten. And we'd doubled our sugar imports, because people had started hoarding.

I didn't "feel" much one way or the other. If I felt anything, it was relief. I thought I'd have to go into some service or other, but I wouldn't be leaving anything behind. I wouldn't be missing anything. I lived alone. I wasn't with anyone. I hated my job. I hated this apartment until Teddy did it up during the war. Managing Billy's money and Carl's didn't take much time. I could still do it, no matter where I was. What difference did war make? My draft board called me to appear. I let my boss know that I'd be going and waited. I just assumed that they'd take me. I took it for granted they took everyone. They didn't take me. Something or other about my eardrums. So I went back to work.

Certainly other things were going on, but they seem hardly worth remembering.

Yes, there was some fuss with Billy about Teddy not signing up, which I still don't completely understand. Don't tell me that's come up again?

What's there to say about it? Teddy didn't want to go, and I agreed with his reasons. He was afraid, and he had good reason to be. Teddy told me what he planned on doing. I told him he'd be mad to sign up or let himself get drafted. There wasn't much to it.

My only involvement was letting Teddy use my apartment during the war. He asked if I'd let him fix it up. I didn't care one way or the other. If Billy did go, Teddy didn't want to stay in that huge place they had over on Park Avenue.

I finally did go to work for the government. My employer had some pull in Washington, and he landed a good job with the OPA in Washington and took me along as part of his staff. I didn't stay with him long.

By April I was on my way to Washington and glad of it. I was very tired of New York.

# Wesley Ober

Oh, yes, I'm feeling fine. They kept me in that evil-smelling hospital for four days and couldn't find a thing wrong with me. Everything ticking along just fine. Just that dizziness from time to time. And I get tired more easily. Probably too much jacking off.

Oh, you've run into a blank wall on Teddy's joining up, have you? Not surprising.

Have you ever read Muriel Spark's *Memento Mori*? Do! It will explain why you've hit a dead spot. Old regrets, old feuds, old enmities don't fade away with time. We're old, but we're not without passionate feelings and strong memories. And the older one gets the more vivid old passions seem. I've no idea why that's so. Perhaps we felt more strongly then than we have since. Perhaps it's maturity. Perhaps it's hardening of the arteries.

Oh, everybody got involved in Teddy's decision, as if it was anybody else's business. But everybody took sides. High drama all around.

What difference did it make? Billy acted as if Teddy aspired to be president of General Motors and being 4-F would ruin his chances.

From what you say, Teddy never did tell Billy that Mamselle Gusmin told Teddy in no uncertain terms not to go in.

Sure, Teddy fucked his life up pretty badly during the war, but that was built into Teddy's life, in a way. Teddy had been feeling less important all the time. He stopped caring about himself.

On December seventh I was down in Malibu, where I'd been summoned by a particularly vicious little starlet who was claiming to be pregnant by me. I had plugged her once in the course of duty. She'd seen too many movies. In thirties movies it took only one fuck to get a woman pregnant. I resented her taking up the one day I had to be with my lover.

I was thirty-five or so at the time, and besides the occasional starlet for political reasons, I was having a lovely affair with a fellow over at Warners. I met him through Carl and Jimmy. He played thugs. Very butch on the screen. He had the most wonderfully sinister face. He was the most urbane, charming man one could know.

The darling little starlet of December seventh (let's call her Thelma, because I think it's a resoundingly ugly name) was currently Queen Cooze on the Universal lot, and I'd been loaned to Universal for a part in *The Mystery of Marie Roget*. Mind you, I don't think Thelma had made a movie, but she'd done a few spreads in the movie mags and more than a few spreads for assorted Universal executives. Thelma could make life very messy for me during my stay at Universal, so when she called me in tears to say she was *enceinte* by me, I dutifully went off to Malibu to console her and negotiate the cost of having her revirginized.

The only reason I'd even met her was that one of her boyfriends at Universal needed a beard. I was to take Thelma to the premiere of *Sergeant York* while the executive took his wife. I was then to fade at the premiere party as soon as the executive got rid of his wife. When his wife didn't go, I was stuck with Thelma. The executive told me none too subtly that he'd appreciate it if I'd see Thelma home and, to thank me for my help, he told me, "Throw one to her." It was his way of saying thank you, and you just didn't turn down poontang proferred by a studio executive.

So, on that fateful day, I was down in Malibu negotiating the cost of an abortion. Thelma claimed that her abortion was going to cost a thousand dollars, when everyone knew that the price was five hundred dollars, even for MGM stars. Since I was due to start shooting *Roget* that week, I didn't want old Thelma giving a piece to some stagehand to have him drop a Klieg on me. It had been done. Ah, the things I went through for art.

I remember that Thelma and I were arguing to a musical tribute to Russ Columbo on the radio when a very excited announcer broke in to announce that the Japs had attacked Pearl Harbor.

Now, Thelma knew that whatever that meant it must be important, because they had broken in on Russ Columbo. She called one of her executives at Universal and asked "Daddy" if that "Jap crap" would stop shooting at the studio. When he told her it wouldn't she seemed very relieved, and we went back to haggling.

We settled on six hundred dollars.

As my lover of the time said, "That's one time you should have looked a gift whore in the mouth."

The day after Pearl, RKO sent a memo around to its contract people asking us to be sure that any of us who were eligible were registered with our local draft boards. I guess that's when I began to sense that the attack on Pearl meant anything.

The headlines said war, Roosevelt said war, and the studios announced a slew of war titles—no scripts or casts, just titles. War seeped into my life out there. It didn't flood in. Little by little I was at war.

Carl fought to keep Jimmy out of it, Billy fought to get Teddy in, Robert just went. The first real sense I had of the war was when Technicolor couldn't supply the stock for a movie I was going to be in. I'd never seen myself in color and I was deeply disappointed, but for the first time I understood that things were really changing.

I couldn't imagine what I would do in a war. I couldn't imagine myself aiming a gun at anything. I'd go hunting with my father and never bring home a thing. I'd just aim above whatever poor thing was on the horizon.

It was between movies in February, and the studio asked me to organize a show for servicemen at a base near L.A. There was a lot of talent around and it wasn't hard to do. I suppose they picked me because I had a background in live theater. Also, I knew a lot of people who could help and I got along well with most of them, and they'd be willing to do me a favor.

I got in touch with the base and worked with some of the officers trying to figure out what the guys would like. I never did find out what the guys would like, but I soon learned that the officers would welcome some of the more "agreeable" starlets.

I was still pissed off with Thelma about saddling me with her abortion so I personally delivered her to the general on the base the night of the show. A wise move. Old Thelma's performance on the mattress must have been a lot better than her rendition of "I Get a Kick Out of You," because the general called to thank me personally. It had been dawning on me that I'd have to do something in the war, so I asked him if the army had any need for a regular supply of shows, and if I might not be just the person to do the job. I was, and I've never begrudged the six hundred dollars to Thelma.

Much to everyone's surprise, it was arranged that I go into the army as a colonel.

But that all happened very slowly. Before I left I made a movie at RKO that shall remain nameless, because I can't for the life of me think of what it was called, but in it I'm one of the local townspeople gathered in a barbershop to shoot the shit, when this newsboy goes by screaming "Japs attack!" There's a great surge of music and we all dash from the shop. Cut to camera panning down the train-station platform at the faces of the men who'd been in the barbershop. We looked grimly determined to go out and get those little yellow Nips. Cut to the same group aboard troop ship talking about Mom, the girl back home, apple pie, hot dogs, and several other matters that seem absolutely demented reasons for going to war. It's a wonder those movies didn't produce desertions.

But off we went, one by one. And I didn't know one gay man—save Teddy—who didn't go. For a gay man to serve meant double jeopardy. Once they were in, there was a thing called "a discharge under conditions other than honorable." And I saw some guys tossed out that way, even though they had distinguished records.

Yes, the war touched us, sometimes in awful ways.

# Carl Mason

I've spent the past week trying to find a way to tell you about my war experiences. It hadn't occurred to me when I agreed to talk with you that I'd have to disguise the details of something I'm very proud of, because I'm speaking as a homosexual. The work I did during the war is one of my proudest memories, but to tell you about it, I have to alter all the facts. After all these years, I still don't want those people I worked with to know that I'm gay, because I know I earned their respect in those years. And I know some of them well enough to know that even now, they'd never speak to me again if they found out about me, found out I'm gay, no matter how good my work was.

I'd so much like to be able to tell exactly what I did, whom I worked for, take credit for things I'm proud of, associations I cherish. I can't, can I?

I'm feeling a little sorry for myself, and for a change I think that's justified.

I was doing my homework for you last night, reading the memoirs some of my associates wrote of those years we worked together. One of them listed the men he said he was proud to be associated with. He named them and thanked them for being an important and cherished part of his life. In a way, I must disown them, and I don't know whether it is to spare their feelings or my own. I had no idea this kind of question would arise for me. Do you know how painful it is?

I remember when I decided I'd have to do something in the war or go bonkers. It was some time in April, and I was sitting by the Warners tank where I'd done most of my crying for Jimmy when it struck me that I'd probably filled that damned tank with my tears, and I started to laugh hysterically at that not-very-funny idea. But it was a turning point.

111

I called around to friends in other studio music departments to see if they were being asked to make any films for the Army or Navy, or whether they were doing volunteer concerts, or whatever. I found that some of us—the music people, that is—had joined up and that others were volunteering their time to provide scores for some Army films one of our big directors was making. I found out whom to contact, got permission from Jack Warner to go lend a hand in Washington for a while, and took off.

Billy was already settled in Washington, so I was able to stay with him for a while. He'd been lucky and had gotten this extraordinary flat in this very posh apartment building in Washington. Beautiful, baronial place. I was very fortunate. Washington was jammed with thousands upon thousands of people who'd flooded in, and most were living in improvised boardinghouses, several people to a room, even sleeping in shifts. Billy had a talent for getting hold of the best—and assuming everyone lived as he did. Billy has always lived by the assumptions of the rich.

Of course, Teddy wasn't with him. Teddy had taken over Robert's little place in New York. I guess that's what Teddy wanted. At all events, Billy had rented their huge place on Park Avenue to some VIP and his family. Very classy people who ruined the place.

I had a lovely room at Billy's.

The first thing I had to do in Washington was get myself hired as a Civil Service Assistant, which was the only way the director could use me, even if I was going to give them my services for nothing.

I wasn't able to do much useful work while I was in Washington, but I found out what was needed and went back to the Coast to line up recording, dubbing, and sound facilities at the majors. The Army films would have to use any free time these facilities had, but it would have to be done on some regular, orderly basis, or we would never be able to get anything finished on time. I worked out a schedule with Twentieth and RKO and my own studio for fixed times and lined up musicians and technicians to donate their time as soon as work could get started on the tracks. Everyone wanted to help, so it all went very smoothly.

I spent the next few years shuttling between Warners and Washington, working some weeks in the superb facilities at the studio and other weeks in a makeshift production studio that was furnished with equipment literally stolen from wherever we could lay hand to it. I've never enjoyed my work more. But I must say that I found the studio work trivial compared to the work on documentaries.

The production schedule for the service films was horrendous. Most of them weren't feature length, but we were doing them in extraordinary quantities.

I felt quite mad at times. We were constantly editing documentary footage, sorting through mile after mile for footage that would illustrate our scripts. There were no tidy scripts. We were editing reality. We were sorting through the first comprehensive visual record of a war. Of course, we didn't think of it that way at the time. Little of what we needed could be staged, and when we did try, it looked incredibly phony next to the real thing. Some was staged, it had to be, but our films drew on the real stuff of life, and those films still look immediate and compelling.

In some perverse way, I think I looked at so much combat footage in the hope of seeing Jimmy somewhere in the masses of men that moved past those hundreds of cameras in the field. And God help me if I had seen him, because I saw hundreds of men torn apart on the screen. But that wasn't an age for chic violence. Carnage—even real carnage—was something to be shunned, and the thought of presenting it to an audience was out of the question. We didn't push that material on the public. It was a kind of restraint that seems most awfully dated—prudish even—but it still makes sense to me.

The memories of all that footage stayed in my head and I could put the feelings it gave me into my scores. My music for those movies wasn't cheap catchpenny tunes orchestrated for a hundred pieces. We used smaller orchestras for those films, but they played music of substance.

And, as I said, as soon as I caught up with my work on those Army films, I would shuttle back to the studio to score some antiseptic piece of patriotic nonsense. I scored an appendix operation aboard a submarine and lines like, "It's the little people who'll win this war."

I went back and forth, from reality to inanity.

The best music I ever wrote is mostly lost in some vault. Who wants to see patriotic documentaries made for a war people believed in, when there's no such thing as a just war anymore?

I almost got lost in work. Not entirely, but almost.

I got one last call from Jimmy before he was shipped over. It was in April . . . April of '42.

To this day, I've no idea where he was calling from, or how he got to make the call. He told me he was being sent overseas. He said they had sailing orders, but he had no idea to where. What an awful call. He said he wasn't alone, and I hated whoever was with him, and, can you believe it, I was jealous of whoever it was. I was sure he was having an affair, that he was with a lover. But of course I couldn't say that. Instead, I asked about the weather. I told him about our weather. When he asked about his mother, I told him that I'd hired someone to look after the old bitch, and then we fought, and ended by hanging up on one another in anger. I don't think I even told him I loved him. But I'd never been as angry with him. He was leaving me, and he needn't have.

That's too many regrets for one day. Let's cut it short. You can come back tomorrow if you want.

Take this with you. It's a recording of the track of *Yankee Doodle Dandy*. Jimmy's on it. God help me, I'm making a very sentimental gesture and I feel embarrassed. I'm feeling very sentimental these days.

Come back tomorrow at three, if that's convenient.

# Billy Hicks

In an absolutely blazing reversal of conventional Army wisdom,
I was assigned to do what I was good at doing: I was assigned to
the Quartermaster Corps and given the job of decorating offices
for the brass in the new Pentagon building.

I'd made some calls to clients I thought might help get me a
useful job in the service, but from what I was hearing about the
way things worked I was sure that my efforts would land me in a
flag-making factory.

I'd never been to Washington until the war, and I've only been
back twice since. It wasn't a hard war for me, though I bitched as
much as anyone about things.

I was really very lucky all down the line. I even got a truly
gorgeous apartment right off the bat.

The apartment was in the Hotel 2400, *the* place to live in those
days, and a lot nicer than some broom closet in the Hay-Adams.
I got the place because the tenant—a vastly rich lady—thought
it best to beat a hasty retreat out of Washington when the war
started. It seems the lady was a good deal more than a run-of-
the-mill pacifist, and had been a staunch supporter of Germany
and Hitler right to the bitter end. She was the pride of the
German Embassy, and she helped a lot of American corporations do business with Nazi cartels, even when it became clear
that it wouldn't be long before we went to war with them.

She was a charming, extraordinarily rich lady, but a little
quirky. When I moved into the apartment I found all two dozen
dining-room chairs had needlepoint swastikas on the seats. A
little *riche* even by Washington's peculiar standards.

She was very wise to beat a retreat to Bermuda till the whole
thing blew over.

She would have just gone off and left the apartment empty, if

115

Lily hadn't convinced her that the apartment would be a lot safer with me in it. Lily also added that if the place were empty, the government might take it into their heads to requisition it. How nice Jewish Lily ever got to know that Nazi-booster is still beyond me. Lily told me the lady was Jewish, but I'm sure she was kidding. Maybe not.

Washington . . . looked very different in those days. I suppose that the gesture was mostly symbolic, but they turned off the lights on all the public buildings. Most nights those massive white monuments looked ghostly, but when there was a full moon, the city had a haunting, eerie glamour. Architecturally, the city is really rather gaudily tasteless, but I must say I grew to love it in those years.

It seems odd to think about today, but they actually stripped all the art from the city, sending it God knows where. They emptied the National Gallery and all the historical documents were sent into hiding. And can you imagine gun crews stationed on the tops of buildings?

The Pentagon was being built at an incredible clip, and there was me running about in the debris planning generals' offices. I soon learned that all generals are not created equal. Some got leather, some got a synthetic look-alike that was just slightly better than oilcloth. I really wasn't at all sure what would suit a general. I knew that I'd have to put a bar in every office, but beyond that I was completely at sea.

In New York, I'd sit down with clients and interview them, visit their present homes. But, for instance, when I tried to get in to interview General Marshall about his new office, I was very rudely put in my place. Any time anyone didn't want to do something during the war, they'd say, "Don't you know there's a war on?" And I'd say, "What the hell do you think I'm doing in this ugly uniform?"

I got nowhere talking to anyone, so I just sat down and made a list of things I thought were very butch—leather, mahogany, gaming prints, books, English brasses, hopsacking. I did find out that all military men were very fond of maps—lots of maps—so, I rigged up all manner of means for displaying maps. Maps rolled up, down, and sideways from the most unexpected places. And they loved having conferences, so I put nice little conference areas in every office. I gave them wardrobe rooms and closets. I spent a fortune to achieve the drabbest effect
‎‑‑‑andal about Harold Ickes's

luxurious offices, I was damned if my work was going to look expensive, no matter how much I spent.

Once I got the pattern down, it was the easiest thing in the world to put one of those offices together, so I started doing a little moonlighting for some Washington clients.

Being someone's interior designer is as good as being their accountant. One learns the most intimate secrets. One general was the worst clotheshorse, and I had to put in all kinds of extra storage for his boring wardrobe of uniforms. He was a one-man road company of *The Student Prince*. Another general got a convertible sofa for exactly the reason one would think. One got elaborate locks on the inside of his door for when he was entertaining his current favorite lieutenant. One got a bar that would have served the Plaza. Another got screening facilities for those awful old-time porno movies with men in black ankle socks and masks. Not that any of them was up to anything new, but I always got a chuckle out of seeing them in full drag on the parade fields, looking the very picture of patriotic probity.

I missed Teddy a lot, but if there was little for him to do in New York, there would have been a lot less in Washington. Besides, Teddy wanted to stay in New York, and I was still miffed over the way he stayed out of service. Well, he loved New York. He never seemed to feel safe anywhere else.

But he wasn't all that bored. At least, he needn't have been. Lily had as much work for him as he cared to do, and by that time, I'd given up on that battle. If he wanted to sew for her, that was up to him. And then there was Robert's apartment, which he was redoing. And to be completely honest, I'd never been able to do anything about his drinking while I was living with him. I was certainly in no position to do anything about it from Washington, and had no intention of having the problem down there with me.

You'll probably be told that I was a major contributor to Teddy's downfall. I certainly know that Robert would like to think that, but that doesn't work, that doesn't hold water.

Have you ever loved somebody who was bent on destroying himself? Most of us do, somewhere along the line in our lives. That's part of their appeal. Most of us are convinced that we can save the person, that we're powerful enough to save them from themselves, that love will make a difference. It never does, I've never seen it, and we just stand around while they go under, until we begin to feel we're going under too and let go.

Robert was in Washington while I was, and Carl would come through every now and then. And Wesley was in and out like a jack-in-the-box doing something or other at the Stage Door Canteen. And when I could work my schedule to have a day or so free, I'd get Teddy to come down or I'd go up. But as much as I loved him, I began to dread his visits, and made less and less effort to free my time up. If I was going to work things out with him, that would have to wait till after the war. It was too messy, too complicated to handle then.

None of us could stop what was happening to him. We all tried. Just ask them. And I could be less help than any of them, because I loved him so terribly that I had to keep my hands off him or kill him for what he was doing to himself . . . what he was doing to us.

# Robert Regal

Bushwah!

What war? That wasn't a war in any encompassing sense. To be sure, we sent a lot of men overseas. A lot of them fought. Yes, a lot of them died. But you can't say America went to war.

I was unfortunately well placed to know what was going on. Those who were well enough to fight went. The rest stayed home and most did very well off the war.

I was in a position to know what effect the war had on this country. Our standard of living actually rose during the war period. Millionaires were made with relative ease. The government built eighteen billion dollars' worth of factories for the thirty or so companies that got over half of all war contracts, and then sold them to those companies for a song. And I shared in that prosperity. So did Carl and Billy. It would have been ingenuous, not to say stupid, not to use the information I had. It was the same information everybody had. I knew how to use it reasonably well, and the money I managed for us became a matter of some substance. Wesley chose to fritter his away, which accounts for his current state.

But we all did well from the war.

If I was well placed to get helpful information, Billy was better placed. Billy has what is called a "knack." Between Lily's contacts and those Billy developed at the Pentagon there was a constant flow of useful information.

Once a week Billy would entertain at that vast apartment of his. I was there almost every week. Good food was hard to come by. I hesitate to think how Billy got the things he served. The table was laden with an extraordinary amount of food and usually things the radio and newspapers told us we were doing without for the good of our country. I noticed, because the boardinghouse where I lived would have had an attack of patriotic ire at the sight of Billy's dinners. None of Billy's guests seemed to find any of the lavishness out of the ordinary.

The information would flow across the table. I heard a lot about orders for goods, shortages, plans for new weapons. Since no one ever said that it was off the record or secret, I couldn't see any moral reason for not acting on what I knew.

I know that Carl and Billy and Wesley feel they were in a war, but I don't. And I'm not speaking solely of the matter of uniform. There's not a scar on any of us. . . . I didn't go to war. I did a job. I did it well. But nonetheless, a job.

There was so little awareness of war that they had to dream things up to make people feel there was a war on. They had us cutting out both ends of tin cans and flattening them. Then we'd put them out to be picked up by Boy Scouts. We had to turn our empty toothpaste tubes in to get another full one. We were limited to two pounds of meat a week. A beer "shortage" was created.

My department was in the middle of the greatest lot of nonsense of all. The OPA [Office of Price Administration] was in charge of a national rationing scheme. We administered the rationing of food and shoes and gasoline. Rationing was done with coupons. You needed a coupon to get a pair of shoes, and so many coupons for beef, so many others for veal or a can of soup. Most people were rationed to three gallons of gas a week.

Every month we printed three and a half billion stamps and every month people would figure out three and a half billion ways to get around the system.

Among the jobs I had with OPA was one as a Chief Investigator. I'd go around and sniff out fraud, and I found so much that I could only deal with the really major ones or ones that would get publicity, because the only reason we went after little fraud was to deter other small defalcations.

For the right money, anyone could have anything they wanted, rationing or not. The only real shortage in America was *Life* magazine, because their paper supply was frozen at a prewar limit.

"Frozen" was an important word during the war. Lots of things were frozen at certain limits. Wages were frozen: You couldn't get a raise. People were frozen in jobs: They couldn't change their jobs.

There was a lot of traffic in rationing stamps. They could be

sold for very good money. A rationing stamp for shoes was
worth a dollar. Meat stamps might bring a dime or quarter,
depending. There was very little need to counterfeit stamps,
because real ones could be gotten very easily.

As I said, one of my jobs was finding these frauds. The
commonest way to get real rationing stamps was for a bank
clerk to go into collusion with a fence for the stamps. A store
owner would deposit the stamps, just as he would cash; the bank
clerk would credit them to the owner's account, and then the
clerk would steam the stamps off the deposit sheet and sell them
to a fence.

Simplest thing in the world.

With three and a half billion produced every month, how in
the world could anyone hope to keep track of the things? And as
I said, the whole rationing thing was mostly a gesture. It was
supposed to make people aware that there was a war on.

The worst scandal was in the OPA itself. I'll have to word this
carefully because I have no idea about whether there's a statute
of limitations on even such an old swindle.

The biggest fraud was wholly the idea of an odious young
lawyer who got attached to OPA to avoid the draft. I'm not
being slanderous. He was fond of telling people about his
influential friends and how he avoided the draft.

If you must give him a name, call him Seymour. He was a
lawyer. He had the makings of a shyster. That's what he became.

I want it to be clear that some of what I'm telling you is
hearsay. Gossip had it that he was from a rich family. First-
generation money. After he'd been in Washington a while, he
was supposed to have been involved in a call-boy-service
scandal. His family got him out of that. It didn't cost them
much, because there were a lot of military men who were said to
have used the service he ran. However, two things did result.
Seymour's family disowned him, and he met a military man who
was to involve him in the McCarthy hearings. . . . Seymour
was among McCarthy's associates.

I can only imagine that he conceived his peculation, because
without family funds or income from his escort service, he
needed money to support a very lavish life style. Lavish by the
standards of most twenty-four-year-olds, which is what he was
at the time.

Oh, yes, Seymour was indeed gay, but since I didn't go to any
bars or gay parties, there was no reason why we should have

met. Billy met him once at a party some senator gave. Even Billy was put off by him. Interestingly, Seymour was inclined to be vociferously antigay around the office. He didn't fool many people. Most certainly the secretaries weren't fooled.

People were reserved around Seymour, because he frightened them. I'm very hesitant to characterize him, but I don't see how I can make the matter clear otherwise: Seymour was evil.

As I said, I imagine that he concocted the fraud because he needed money.

It was a simply executed fraud. It involved the printing of the stamps. The engravings for the stamps were made by the Treasury, but they were not printed by them. They were printed elsewhere. That was the problem in security. That was Seymour's opportunity.

It was one of Seymour's jobs to collect the first sheets of test engravings from a run and go over them to be sure that there were no printing errors. He was then to approve them and deliver them to the printer with his "okay for printing."

But Seymour merely had to phone over his approval of the run to the printer. There were too many steps to the procedure.

Engraving plates have relatively short lives, so new plates were constantly being prepared. New runs were frequent. In this manner, thousands upon thousands of sheets of stamps were removed by Seymour from the printer's on no more than his word, and printing initiated by a phone call. He phoned, despite the fact that procedure called for the sheets to be delivered back to the printer with Seymour's initialed approval.

Seymour got away with this for over two years, and my audit of the fraud couldn't begin to account for what was missing—or, to be accurate, what had been stolen.

Printers are so used to running off dozens of sheets to prove color and the quality of the printing that it was nearly impossible to account for a few sheets of paper. However, in this case, each sheet of paper was eight feet by six, containing thousands of rationing stamps.

Those who defraud share one characteristic: They are early to work, late to leave, and never call in sick. Seymour was a model of punctuality and health.

I found the fraud by accident. Sheets of meat-ration stamps started showing up without glue on their backs. It was my job to requisition glue, so I got the call to check with the printer.

We couldn't resolve the problem on the phone, so I went to the shop and asked to see a sample of the approved sheets. There were none. Seymour never turned them over.

Fraud is very common, and the bigger the fraud the less inclined the organization robbed is to make it public. Corporations won't usually do it, because prosecuting calls into question the protections exercised to safeguard assets. The government rarely does it, because they fear looking foolish.

I duly reported my discovery, after doing a preliminary audit. As nearly as I could tell, the potential profit to Seymour for the likely number of stamps he absconded with was in the range of from seven million dollars to twelve million dollars.

After I submitted my report, I became *persona non grata*. It doesn't do to be the bearer of bad tidings. Seymour was gone within two days and my boss at the OPA called me into his office about a week later.

He began by saying that he was grateful for my discreet handling of the information. (I'd let no one else know.) He said the magnitude of the fraud was such that it was now being discreetly handled at the very highest levels. I took this to mean that the matter would be buried.

I was told that I should destroy my files on my investigation and that my conscientiousness was going to be rewarded with a plum job at several thousands of dollars a year more. I was being gotten rid of.

I told him how gratified I was. I told him that I would see to destroying the files and all relevant material that very morning.

It is the single most uncharacteristic action of my life that I didn't destroy a thing. I packed up my files and some incriminating material I found in Seymour's files, and moved them to my room in the boardinghouse on my lunch hour.

They proved very useful to Carl and Wesley when they got entangled in that McCarthy mess. I hated having to use them. It went very much against my grain.

I hope you're noticing that I'm trying to be more talkative. Your friend Wesley gave me a good talking to about not cooperating with you. Wesley knows I'm not talkative. Why I'm included is beyond me. Wesley could tell you everything. He has a memory like an elephant.

What is this, your ninth or tenth visit?

Twelfth?

My God, I've been talking a lot.

I hope I'm not starting to enjoy this kind of thing. I know too many people who are nothing but talk.

# Wesley Ober

I couldn't have gotten a better job during the war. Organizing shows and doing liaison work with the Stage Door Canteen and Hollywood Canteen was just my cuppa. I was full of energy and enthusiasm, I was doing very useful war work, and before you applaud, let me say that I was getting laid with absolutely astounding frequency. I really should have been an agent or producer, because I loved those tax-free benefits.

Organizing talent to entertain troops gave a lovely patriotic patina to all the fucking. Can you imagine! I was interviewing talent for dozens of touring companies and working with entertainment officers on bases all over the country and overseas. To paraphrase Will Rogers, "I never met an entertainment officer I didn't love." And for those of different tastes, I supplied enough poopsies to assorted officers to make me dearly loved in every theater of operation around the globe.

I must have gotten something of a reputation. The Disney studio used to design emblems for the services, and a friend of mine over there designed one for me. It was a dancing cock, brandishing a straw hat and cane. Teddy embroidered it for me and I wore it sewn inside my jacket.

The war was a lot of different things for me. I had many affairs, lots of one-nighters, but I knew what was happening. I'd go out with some of the shows to break them in—to front-line bases, to hospitals. I got to know our boys. The war was a different and difficult experience for them. Most were the children of the Depression. They knew that kind of hardship, but not the hardship of war, and not foreignness. They experienced the Depression with the support of family and friends. They didn't have that kind of soul support at war. Most were provincial, and so was I, or so I'd been. Americans don't transplant easily to foreign soil. I think we tend to feel displaced, to feel uneasy about foreignness.

I suppose all servicemen talk of home, but all I remember being asked when I was overseas was, "How are things at home?"

Hospital shows were the hardest to get through. The performer would get on stage and whoop it up, and pretend it was all the greatest fun in the most ordinary of circumstances. I remember I had Carole Landis with one of my shows, and we had to send her home. It was too rough on her. I forget why, but we were alone one night after a hospital show, and Carole said to me, "I feel like a fraud in front of them. I'm up there peddling my ass and waving my tiny tits around, and I know that some of them are never going to fuck again, or touch a tit, or walk. And the poor bastards are going along with the gag. And there I am singing away, and all I want to do is stand in the middle of the stage and weep for them."

I was thirty-five when the war started and thirty-eight when it ended, so most of the boys looked—well, like boys, like children, to me.

It was never hard to find the gay officers, or the gay servicemen. They're right: It does take one to tell one. And they were as displaced as any of the others. They had the same odds of surviving as anyone, and they had every bit as much to live for as any of the others.

I felt very fatherly toward a lot of them. To be sure, I fucked with them, but in a fatherly way.

I think the only time the gay men really felt their difference was when the other men went whoring or got drunk and decided to go out and beat up some fags. Not to participate in such all-American pastimes would have been "chicken" or worse. So some gay men did both.

I only had one affair during the war. It was early on, and I never repeated the mistake.

I fell quite madly in love with a lieutenant. Like myself, he was a North Carolina boy, from Raleigh, and he was almost the spitting image of my rustic love, Bernard. I've always had a penchant for the long-boned, wiry types. I'm sure there was a little flirting, but as I remember, we just fell into one another's arms. We met at the Hollywood Canteen and I got him dances with Ann Sheridan and Adele Jergens, just so he'd have something to write home about, and then I whisked him off to my place.

He was twenty-two. He knew me from some of my movies, which seemed to impress the hell out of him. He couldn't remember what they were, but neither could I.

We fucked, my dear. We fucked his leave away, and when we felt that sanity dictated a little food we'd dash off to the Brown Derby for abalone and I'd call around to see if I could round up a star or two to dine with us! I invited no men. He was mine. I was in love.

I've never understood why most people turn painful memories into amusing stories. I do it. I think I do it for fear of being boring. I've never been able to turn that time with him into a good story. The jokes go limp.

I'm not one to run around giving myself wholeheartedly to affairs. He was different.

I've loved, dear heart, I've loved.

I saw his train off, which was probably an awful idea, because we just stood looking at one another and sobbing helplessly, both of us. To hell with what people thought.

They must have moved him East and right overseas. He made a profound impression on me and, hard to credit, I remained celibate until I got the news of his death. It was only five weeks.

He'd been raised by an aunt who'd died, so he left me his veteran's insurance. I spent it on the most extraordinary amount of black-market Taittinger.

After that, I restricted my activities to casual lust. Love seemed much too perishable.

I was well into my second childhood before I let myself go again, but then I could excuse my lapse on the grounds of oncoming senility.

# Carl Mason

I'd stand there with one eye on the orchestra and one on the screen and conduct, and it got so I couldn't tell one movie from another. They all began to look alike to me, as I'm sure they did to the audience. It was as if Warners had a "make-a-war-movie kit," and they'd just reassemble all the same pieces into different combinations. It was rather more like watching a serial than separate movies.

To give the actors their due, they did the parts without looking embarrassed. What a collection! Alan Hale, George Tobias, Raymond Massey, Dane Clark, Sam Levene, Helmut Dantine, Peter Lorre, Victor Francen, Claude Rains—all remarkably able, civilized men, but all playing the same people over and over. It didn't matter whether Dane Clark played a character called "Brooklyn," "Bronx," or "Canarsie." They were all the same—tough and lovable.

I've looked up some of the lines from those movies, so I quote with accuracy. Here's a lovely one: "We're going to play 'The Star-Spangled Banner' with two-ton bombs." Or, perhaps my favorite: "Was that cannon fire, or is it my heart pounding?"

I knew I'd worked on too many of those things when I spent half a day rescoring some scenes we'd recorded the week before. Someone in the scheduling department made a mistake and the same footage was sent through a second time and I conducted the whole lot without suspecting that I'd done it before. I was very tired, but so was the material.

But it really didn't make any difference. The audiences went anyway. Perhaps there's a kind of comfort in sameness.

It was August '42 before I heard a word from Jimmy, and that preyed on my mind. I thought that I'd completely alienated him.

I knew that I should have behaved better when he called, but that was hindsight.

I couldn't bring myself to call his mother to find out how he was, and I couldn't write. How could I repair a lovers' quarrel in a letter I feared would be censored? I left it alone, and I was busy enough then with two jobs not to have time to dwell on it.

I remember that his letter finally came from New York. It came in a handwritten envelope with a New York City return address I didn't recognize.

> My dearest Carl:
>
> I'm going to write this, but you may not get it for a while, since I'll wait to get it hand-carried to the States and mailed from there. I'm trying to find a "friendly" censor (read "gay"), but no luck as yet.
>
> I know that you're jealous, but that was no reason to act like such a silly jackass when I called you. I don't know why I keep giving you assurances that I'm faithful when you never believe me, but I always was and I still am. So, my darling, no more scenes on the phone. You don't know what it does to me. I know you're sorry ten minutes later, but I'm not just out on the patio these days so we can make up right then and there.
>
> I hate writing to you, because I don't want to write, I want to hold you, and I don't want to have to say a thing.
>
> There's not much news, unless a lot of waiting around is news. They've gotten us here—Gibraltar, that is—and here we sit like the damned seagulls that seem to be everywhere. There's talk about going into North Africa. There's other talk about Italy and the south of France, but there's more talk about North Africa, where the war news isn't so hot. By the time you read this, we should be somewhere or other, or I'll be buried under seagull do.
>
> We had one of your movies last night and there was your name in the credits. I always feel so proud when I see your name up there. We were still together when you were working on it. You were right. Jane Wyman is the best thing in it. You said it wasn't very funny, which may explain why I cried all the way through it. Actually, I think your music did that. I was with Herb and Norm—a couple of "special" friends—so they understood. How they've managed to become lovers in the middle of the

army is beyond me, but I fear for them getting caught. You'd like them.

I hate to say it, but I'm not sure that my signing up was one of my hottest ideas. Still, I wouldn't have felt right if I hadn't.

Damn it, my dear, there's no way to get what I want to say onto paper. I've never been away before. I don't miss home, I miss you and I feel as if I'm only half here. Do you know what I mean? Life doesn't feel right without you.

What I'd really like to do is sing for you. Letters aren't my strong point. If I could sing I'd do a medley of "Don't Sit Under the Apple Tree" and "Praise the Lord and Pass the Ammunition," and then I'd break your heart with "My Buddy."

Here goes: "Nights are long since I went away, I think about you all through the day." I feel better already.

I hate to bring this up again, so forgive me before I do. Forgiven? Do be sure that the old girl gets looked after. I know she's a pain, but she is alone and I do worry about her. If you think that fellow you hired is doing a good job, leave it at that. As long as I know it's being done, it will ease my mind about her.

Well, my dearest, you have just read the longest letter I've ever written and one of the few.

"Miss your voice, the touch of your hand."

I had no idea how much I loved you.

Always,
JIMMY

Well, I had one of the great cries of my life over that.

I had a few V-mail letters from Jimmy after that, but they were censored, and what was left on those shrunken letters was pretty innocuous. I wrote a couple of times, mostly movie gossip. But we both hated having to say nothing.

Christmas was coming and I was missing Jimmy and getting sentimental—and feeling guilty that I hadn't been over to see his mother—so I took time out and drove over to her place with a gift from Bullock's and a quart of vodka.

When I got there I saw the flag with the gold star in her window.

Jimmy was dead.

I drove away and then I drove back, and then I drove away again, and then back.

I had no other way of finding out what had happened to him, except to ask her. I don't know why I had to know. It wouldn't have made any difference. That nasty little rayon flag said it all.

I finally parked and went up and walked in.

It seems weird to me that I remember so vividly, but I remember she was sitting in the living room, in a chenille bathrobe, listening to an old radio soap opera called *Pepper Young's Family,* so it must have been in the afternoon. I just stood there like an idiot and looked at her.

I have no idea how drunk she was, or if she even was. I'd like to think she was, because she just stared back at me and after a while she said, "You don't know how happy I am that he can never come back to you."

I just ran, and the last I ever heard of her was her yelling, "Faggot cocksucker."

I don't remember doing it, but I must have called Lily, because she was there a few days later. Just dropped everything and came out to be with me. I didn't know what to say to her about what had happened, any more than I know what to say about it now.

I must have called the studio and told them I was ill, or Lily did. I suppose I just wandered around the house till Lily got there. She got the place in order and I wandered around some more. I don't remember doing anything, or thinking anything. I know I couldn't listen to music. I wanted silence.

Besides, after making music my only interest in life, I knew how much I'd cheated myself before I met Jimmy. It wasn't a question of music or Jimmy. I had both for a while. I couldn't rush back into music and hide.

But that's all hindsight, because I don't remember consciously thinking anything at all.

After five weeks or so, I got up one morning and told Lily I was going to the studio. She just nodded and a couple of days later she went back to New York.

Everyone at the studio was very solicitous about my health. When they'd called the house, Lily had said it was pneumonia, but I heard later that the word was around that I had cancer. I hadn't been eating much, so I imagine I looked pretty washed out.

No one at the studio knew what the reason was. That kind of mourning is for straight people.

I had no sex for over a year. The idea of physical intimacy repelled me, and every time I tried to masturbate I'd start thinking of Jimmy, and that was the end of that.

I did finally meet someone—in late '43, I think it was. He worked for Richard Bales, who put on the concerts at the National Gallery during the war. He was an awfully nice young man, but I was too bruised to let him get too close. But we had some nice times. It was easy. It suited me. I hope it suited him.

I spent a lot of time trying to figure out how to provide some kind of memorial for Jimmy. I needed to give something to his memory. What finally occurred to me was the simplest possible solution. I wrote what I called "My Themes for Jimmy," and used them in one of the wartime films I scored for the Army. I spent weeks trying to figure out how to ask the director to let me put some kind of dedication in the credits, but I never could. So it's just a little more music for a movie.

# Billy Hicks

It never occurred to me to question the fact that I was only twenty-eight years old and a major, and already getting pretty well known, even famous. Perhaps the army couldn't have a lieutenant spending the millions I spent.

My work in the Pentagon gave me the idea for what came to be called "job standard." That meant that lieutenants got one grade of furniture and carpeting, a major a higher grade, and so on up, from venetian blinds for the proletariat to Thaibok silks for generals.

Thank God for the work for civilians I was getting, or I would have been bored out of my mind.

I was working at the top of my form and making a superb reputation—and just having the best time.

By that Christmas in '43 I was doing some work on Blair House and I'd been consulted about doing more work on Dumbarton Oaks for the conference that coming fall. I'd been sworn to secrecy on that. Word couldn't get out that the building was being prepared for a major international conference. Also, I was something of a pet with the local society ladies. I helped them get New York designers to send down clothes for their Stage Door Canteen fashion shows over at the old Belasco Theater. I got them caterers. I got them nylons.

I suppose I stood out because I had a little flair. The service wives and the senators' wives were married to men whose long suit was not flair.

My Christmas party was going to be a high point of the social season, and I was looking forward to it. Both Carl and Wesley were going to be in town at the same time. Robert was coming over. Lily was bringing Teddy down from New York. It was going to be like old times.

I was ten years out of Schenectady and a million miles away.

There it was Christmas Eve, 1943, and I was going to give one of the great parties of the year. A nice Russian I knew over at the embassy had gotten me several pounds of caviar and, God knows how, quarts and quarts of their vodka. I suppose all those ships coming back from Murmansk had to carry something. A Venezuelan I'd gotten to know got cases and cases of prewar Haut Briand. The guest list numbered over a hundred and I'd ordered seventy-five pounds of eye of round. I'd borrowed a chef from the Mayflower Hotel. Mrs. Geaney, the housekeeper at Blair House, whom I'd gotten to know when I did work over there, helped me get dozens of white roses. And she was coming.

*Haut* Washington was coming.

I had a gift for everyone. I'd designed a little key ring that said "Peace in '44" and had Tiffany make me up over a hundred in silver, and every guest would get one. I'd gotten wonderful gifts for my really close friends from the buyers I'd gotten to know over at Garfinckel's.

Wesley was bringing some stud star he was having a fling with, and Carl was bringing that nice musician of his from the National Gallery. Robert's general friend was going to be there—but with wife. People were coming from the Stage Door Canteen, and each was to bring a serviceman as part of the year's "Share Your Home At Christmas" drive.

I'll never forget that night if I live to be normal.

I remember it so vividly because it turned into one of the most nerve-wracking evenings of my life.

The party was due to start at seven and the ice storm hit Washington that morning. Washington could go to pieces with a half-inch of snow. An ice storm brought the city to its knees. That would have been enough to ruin the evening.

Lily and Teddy were due to get a morning train out of New York, but Lily got the flu or something and called to say that she couldn't come, but that Teddy was catching the train alone.

Without Lily along to put some kind of restraint on his drinking, I felt sure that Teddy would show up . . . Well, he did.

Would you believe that *every* guest showed up. Not one missed the party. And after Teddy got there, I wished that no one had shown up.

# Robert Regal

Don't tell me he's still carrying on about that party. He didn't have to cope with anything. All he did was stand around and twitter.

Billy just did what he always does when things get too tough to handle, he turned his back on them. What does he mean by "ruined party"? Not one guest knew what was going on.

To be sure, it was an awful evening, not for Billy, but for Teddy.

I'm very likely to say something I'll regret, so you'd best talk to Wesley about that evening.

Yes . . . feelings can still run high over things like that, even things that happened *that* long ago.

# Wesley Ober

How would you like the story? I can do it as farce or tragedy. Actually, it was more Barbara Cartland, with the kind of inadvertent foolishness she seems to do so well.

Let's set the stage. By that Christmas in 1943 the war was well along. Some even said it would end in '44. Billy had gotten to know just about everyone worth knowing in Washington, and he gave terrific parties. He thought that this might be one of his last in Washington, so he trotted out the top of his guest list and arranged a party that even the *Post* society editor, who hated his guts, was forced to report.

After almost two years of living in that apartment, Billy had turned it into one of the most beautiful homes in Washington. I keep calling it an apartment. It was a whole floor of the building, and of a very sizable building.

When I heard what kind of a party it was going to be, I lined myself up a date to suit the occasion. Let's just call the old darling a "star in uniform". . . and a star out of uniform, I might add. Though I could never be sure *what* uniform. I went over to his place in Beverly Hills one night and he greeted me wearing a WAC's uniform. He also had a WAVE's uniform and also had the military costume Betty Grable wore in *Pin-Up Girl* copied. I got terribly scratched by sequins.

But anyway, there it was, all perfectly arranged. The war was going well, the guest list glittered, the table sparkled, and people arrived in the highest of humors. They'd all had to fight their way through an ice storm, and shared hardship can add a kind of high gaiety. If you've ever been in New York during a blizzard you know what I mean. The guests had gotten there with great difficulty and they were bent on having the time of their lives to make the effort worthwhile.

As I remember, not a single person was even late—but just in case, Billy had had the chef plan on serving an hour later than scheduled. This allowed for an hour's more drinking, and you know what that does to a party.

It all got pretty raucous. My "star date" got groped by a number of highly placed matrons. Robert's general friend got very indiscreet, which very obviously didn't surprise his wife but scared the hell out of Robert, who kept darting away from him like some kind of maddened Cio-Cio-San. The gossip was at high tide and would have done Nero's court credit. All kinds of goodies about a general in lingerie, an admiral over in Walter Reed for a face lift. I was having a terrific time.

I heard the doorbell ring and saw the maid pass the door where I was standing, and didn't think a thing of it. She came into the room like a shot, scurried to Billy, who scooted off after her, and on his way past me he just grabbed me up and took me along.

Teddy had arrived . . . such as he was. The poor bugger was down on his hands and knees in the foyer trying to get up another quart or so. The maid knew better than to stay around for the whole scene, so she bowed out.

Billy just stood there, staring down at Teddy, who just stayed on all fours looking down the mess he'd upchucked. He said, "The train was late."

Billy looked as if he were going to be ill, and he said that he was sorry the train had even arrived. Billy started looking about as bad as Teddy. He just couldn't handle this kind of mess. He never could.

I'll try and get this right.

I bent down to help Teddy up, and he said, "Don't you help me, I want Billy to help me."

Billy said, "I can't." Then Teddy sort of flopped over and leaned against the wall.

And Teddy said, "It's you I want to help me. Don't keep handing me over. If you don't care anymore, please get rid of me."

And Billy said something like "I want to, but I can't."

Well, God knows, at that moment Teddy wasn't the most desirable thing I'd ever seen. He looked as if he'd been kicked to Washington.

Teddy reached into his pocket and took out a small package and handed it up to Billy, who just looked at it and said, "Later."

I told Billy that I'd get Teddy back to a room in the servants' area. It was well out of the way. Teddy could sleep it off and nobody need know. It happens in the best of families.

I helped Billy get our friend to his feet, and Teddy got a second wind and started yelling something about Billy now having the reason he needed to be rid of him for good. Teddy went on in that vein at the top of his lungs while I was trying to lug him down the hall. Not one person came out of the drawing room to see what was going on. Washingtonians know that closed doors are best left closed. But Robert recognized Teddy's voice, and he came out through the dining room.

All Billy could say was, "This is no time to talk," and he kept saying it over and over.

As always, the less solicitous Billy seemed to be toward Teddy, the more solicitous Robert became.

I sent Billy back to his guests, and Robert and I took Teddy off to a servant's room at the back.

Billy could never handle this kind of mess. He just wasn't equipped to. Nothing in his nature made it possible. Billy could make the world do nip-ups. What Billy planned always went well. He loved Teddy, but when Teddy pulled stunts like that Billy panicked. Teddy was untidy. Not always, but sometimes, and Billy never did learn how to handle it. Robert shouldn't be so hard on Billy about that. But then, Robert loved Teddy too, and Robert was a coper. Billy just isn't, not with mess.

And while I'm at it, Teddy's arrival *en déshabillé* was not that unusual an event, so what happened next should have been anticipated. I heard what Teddy said while I was tucking him into bed, and I was so distracted—or drunk—that I didn't pick up on it when Teddy started talking about how he was ruining Billy's life. More fool I.

Let me go back a bit.

When war broke out, Billy was down in Washington in nothing flat. Robert went too, and the place Billy and Teddy had over on Park Avenue was sublet. So Teddy moved into Robert's place, and for a while it looked like this might be all for the best for Teddy.

God help me, I'll try and tell this without any Freudian overlay or Max Steiner background music, but it's not easy. It's just too much of a "classic case" or, closer to the mark, a bad Joan Crawford script.

When Billy left, Teddy bloomed for a while. He seemed

relieved to be alone and out of that big place on Park, and he was very busy redoing Robert's apartment, which Robert had fixed up in Early Auditor. Teddy did the place over, and very charmingly. And Teddy went back to work for Lily. He even stopped drinking for a while. He looked better and sounded better than he had for a long time.

I hated to think that Billy and Teddy were through, but Teddy couldn't go on without even the status of a kept man.

I've no idea why they loved one another so much, because I don't think anyone can understand love from the outside. At least, I never could.

I think Teddy just needed a little space to get in touch with himself again. The years with Billy had been a rush, and Teddy sort of got left a little behind.

I think that it was late in '42 when Teddy quit working for Lily. It was about the middle of the next year—in '43—when I found out how he'd been earning a living.

God knows how they tracked me down. I was in Texas directing some dreary little one-set, four-character play that was going to tour army bases. It was one of those asexual comedies about virgins and soldiers that Army brass felt wouldn't get the boys too excited. It was the dramatic equivalent of saltpeter.

Anyway, the Red Cross found me in Texas and informed me that my "son" was in Mount Sinai Hospital in New York. My son turned out to be Teddy. The Red Cross had arranged for my transportation to New York.

They couldn't tell me much, but I figured that if Teddy was posing as my son, something was very much the matter, so I got up to New York as fast as the rotten train service could get me there.

When I got to his room I could barely see Teddy under all the bandages.

He shouldn't have talked—his jaw was wired and he seemed to be wrapped everywhere—but I sat through a fairly long and painful narrative. He had to tell me all the gruesome details—that's why I was there. He couldn't bring himself to let anyone else know. As he said, Billy couldn't have handled the problem, and Robert would be oversolicitous. He couldn't find Carl. He was ashamed to tell Lily, so that left me.

Teddy had been paying his rent by hustling, and I really can't imagine anyone less equipped for the job than Teddy. Teddy was always handing himself over to people—no questions asked— and he was the most trusting man I think I've ever met. Teddy as a hustler was like casting Mary Pickford in *Rain*.

He'd started drinking again, and his job for Lily didn't pay enough to support his habit, so he'd quit. And the rent on Robert's apartment wasn't all that cheap. He couldn't ask Billy for money. That was partly pride and partly that he knew Billy was pouring all his money into the new fabric business and some other enterprises Billy had started with Lily. Anyway, those are the reasons Teddy gave me.

At all events, Teddy was hustling, and his only asset for the work was the fact that he looked gay. In those days, a lot of gay men couldn't spot another gay guy if he wasn't obvious. Still can't, I suppose.

He'd gotten beaten before. Several times, as a matter of fact, but the last one—an Army major—had really done a job on him.

Teddy had picked him up in the Astor Bar. Now, in its heyday, the Astor Bar was a very classy place. As you went in from Broadway, the gay side of the bar was on your right, the other side was straight. But all very discreet and all the men looking very butch in their military drag. I still can't imagine Teddy in there. He certainly must have stood out.

The major arranged for Teddy to meet him outside the hotel. Teddy said that this was usual, since most of the servicemen he picked up were afraid of being seen with anyone who looked as gay as he did.

Teddy was small. Billy calls him frail. He wasn't. He just wasn't very big. The major was. They both had a good deal more to drink at Teddy's place, and the major's way of getting his money's worth was to beat Teddy senseless.

When Teddy came to, he found ten dollars on a table. The major was a man of honor. Teddy had patched himself together before, after he'd gotten hold of a bad piece of meat, but he knew that he'd need a hospital this time. There was internal damage and he'd been kicked repeatedly in the crotch. Well, he couldn't afford a hospital and he couldn't face one, so he took a bottle of barbiturates.

He didn't have the barbiturates by accident. He'd been giving the matter serious thought. He'd have died if the super hadn't come up to let the exterminator in. They'd gotten him to the hospital.

I spent that day with Teddy, and the next day I arranged some leave and stayed in New York.

I moved into Teddy's apartment, and I'd go over to the hospital every day to see him. I put the apartment back in order—his last encounter had been messy—and gave his super an outrageous bribe to keep him from throwing Teddy out or writing to Robert. I did get hold of Lily and told her what had happened. I knew she'd keep quiet. I couldn't stay in New York indefinitely, and someone had to know what was going on.

I got hold of an actor I know who was a member of Alcoholics Anonymous, and I talked to him about Teddy. He got Teddy to some meetings after he came out of the hospital, but it didn't take.

I suppose I shouldn't admit this, but I'm a snoop, and while I was staying at Teddy's I found a letter I shouldn't have read—and did.

The letter was about a year old. It was from Teddy's mother. Now, remember, they'd sent him off from home without so much as a good-bye—just some money and a bus ticket for when he got out of the hospital.

Well, after all those years, ol' Mum had finally written. I suppose she couldn't wait. Teddy's father had committed suicide. He'd killed himself, the letter said, because he could no longer live with the knowledge that his son was homosexual. He'd gotten very drunk and driven himself into a creek. It seemed a rather belated reaction, coming about ten years after Teddy left home.

I found out that Teddy had been badly beaten five times by other sadistic clients, less badly mauled by a dozen or so, and, as often as not, not even paid for his services.

Obviously, another occupation would have to be found for Teddy. I got hold of Carl and Lily, and we bought him a secretarial course. Obviously more an act of desperation than a decision. I got him to agree to try. As it turned out, it didn't do any good, and Teddy went back to the streets with equally baleful results.

Teddy didn't go back to the Astor Bar, although it would have been better if he had. He started working Grand Central Station.

During the war, Grand Central was a twenty-four-hour mob scene. Trains couldn't be depended upon, so people would just show up and wait till a train was leaving for where they wanted to go. Teddy would get himself up in one of his costumes and wander through the station, getting, he told me, no small amount of flack from the "ladies" who worked the same beat.

The tea room there was always busy. Furtive and dangerous, to be sure, but damned active. Besides the police patrolling and doing a thriving business in entrapment, there were MP's to protect our servicemen from the wiles of men of *pre*verted tastes.

And there was Teddy wandering around that mess, and he just couldn't seem to stop himself. So now, besides being beaten up and ripped off, he was getting himself arrested. Obviously an impossible state of affairs. Impossible, but apparently appealing to Teddy.

Lily tried to save the day. She knew the owner of a rather swank bar on the East Side whom she'd been responsible for making a big success. That is, she steered friends there, encouraged their using the place for private parties, and got the place's name in the columns. Lily, of course, entertained there as a guest of the house. But still, she did put the place on the map. The owner—we'll call him André—was gay. Married, but gay.

Lily had a talk with him and explained about Teddy, and for her continued goodwill and a modest fee she arranged that Teddy be able to cruise the bar for "patrons" without getting any flack. André knew that Teddy would drive off the butcher numbers—and there were complaints about him—but for a while he was safe there. But Teddy didn't want to be safe, so that arrangement didn't last for long.

I suppose that what I'm trying to say is that we tried. We failed, I suppose, because we were trying to get Teddy to do something he didn't want to do.

Teddy was out to wreck himself, and if you've ever had a friend set out to do that, you can't stop them by love, money, or manipulation.

All of which brings us back to that Christmas Eve in Washington. Billy didn't know any of this when Teddy showed up at the Christmas party. I did, and I also knew about two other suicide attempts since that time I went up to New York.

After we got Teddy to bed that night, Robert sat with him for a while, until Teddy fell asleep.

It was hours later when we checked on him again. By then, the serving people had been tipped and given gifts and gone home, and the lot of us old-timers settled in the den over a lot more drinks we didn't need. Around four, Robert went back to look in on Teddy.

Robert found Teddy in a tub of very red water.

Carl and Robert pulled him out.

Robert went off with Teddy in the ambulance. I stayed with Billy.

I saw the tub, and I remember thinking that he just wasn't big enough to have that much blood.

Much as I wanted to spare Billy the sight, I had to leave the tub like that. I just couldn't bring myself to reach in and pull the plug.

Teddy had apparently found out how to do the job right, and he'd sliced down from the wrists towards the crook of his arm. I've no idea how they saved him.

Carl had said he'd call from the hospital when he had any news, so Billy and I just sat around drinking, but the booze couldn't reach us by then.

Billy and I talked for a while, mostly about nothing. All Billy asked me was what I thought he should do about Teddy. If he lived, I suppose he meant.

I'd given that question a lot of thought, but I couldn't tell Billy what my answer was.

You see, if I'd found Teddy that night, I think I would have closed the door on him and let him go, let him finally have some peace.

Some of us just can't pull off being gay. We can't take what people say about us, or how they look at us, or what we're sure they're thinking. Those who get as old as I am are pretty tough.

Around dawn I wandered back to the room where we'd put Teddy, and I unpacked his things and put them away. I found the package Teddy had tried to hand Billy when he arrived. It was a Tiffany watch. Gold case and gold strap. Teddy was trying to keep up. Christ knows what it cost.

I had to go up to New York for a few days' work between Christmas and New Year's, and when I finally got back to Washington I went to see Teddy. When I walked into his room, he looked at me for the longest, saddest moment and said, "Well, I'm back." I got the feeling he'd sooner not have been.

Something changed in Teddy after that last try. He seemed tougher after that, but his extraordinary sweetness was gone. I suppose he just decided that if his friends wouldn't let him kill himself, he'd have to find some way to survive.

He even started wearing suits after that. Billy and Robert were very pleased. Teddy looked almost straight. Well, from the back anyway.

# Carl Mason

I knew the war was winding down when I saw the rough cut of a movie called something like *Getting Back Into the Civilian Swing.* "Swing" was the popular music of that period, and the movie opened with servicemen jitterbugging with a lot of young women, then match-dissolved into those same men dancing in civvies. The movie was a ghastly piece of nonsense full of the most cloying, useless advice about readjusting to civilian life. I gave that film the score it deserved, the musical equivalent of treacle. Louis B. Mayer would have been affronted by my shameless sentimentality.

But that movie was my cue to think about stopping the government work.

Once it was clear, in '45, that Germany was going under, a kind of lassitude settled on America. There didn't seem to be much interest in winning in the Pacific, but we were too far committed to what was called "unconditional surrender" to back down out there and just settle for a negotiated peace.

My rather casual affair with my friend at the National Gallery had pretty much run its course, and often I didn't even call him when I was in Washington.

By and large, I was bored. At least I was bored with the present, so I started looking toward the future when this whole mess would be over.

Even the few films we were making that featured the awful carnage of battle had lost their power to touch me. I'd seen too much. My eye was numb to it.

I was very happy when Warners asked me if I'd go to Moscow early in '45 to work with some Russian movie people who were getting back into full-scale production. I was to be part of a team of technical and creative people who were to advise Mosfilm on the building of new sound facilities in Moscow now that the Germans had retreated and they could go back.

The Army was to fly the team over, and, to orient us, a cultural attaché from the Russian embassy in Washington came to Hollywood to explain what was needed and to show us some Russian movies.

I'd never seen a Russian film. I knew Shostakovich had written a film score and I'd heard that Prokofiev was working on one for Eisenstein, and that's all I knew.

The attaché began by showing us a Russian musical, their equivalent of an Alice Faye vehicle. Vehicle was the word, because the musical was called *Tractor Driver*. It really was. (We nicknamed it *Tractor Drivel*.) I learned that the Russians had made wide use of movies ever since Stalin realized how potent they were as propaganda. Movies were all under state control, and if Russians couldn't get to the movies they brought the movies to them by truck and even boat.

Off we went in our hollowed-out B-29 to Moscow, where the lot of us were greeted with great ceremony by a man named Alexandrov, who was czar of film production.

The technical people spent hard days trying to be helpful through translators who were damned near useless because they had no technical vocabulary, and our tech people were further stymied by the Russians' sound system, which had basic differences from the American and used equipment that was a decade or more out of date. The Russians had standardized on something called the Tager System.

I spent my days with the musicians. I was a good deal more comfortable, because I had a translator who understood music. The musical high point of my trip was meeting Prokofiev. We met at Mosfilm where he'd come for a meeting with Eisenstein, who was making *Alexander Nevsky* at the time. I thought it was an awful movie when I finally saw it, but that score is incredible.

I worked with the orchestra and their sound people, showing them what we'd learned about mike patterns and orchestration that was giving us a fuller sound with more depth and balance.

The only thing I regret about that trip is a brief liaison I had with a cellist. And it is a long-standing and very vivid regret. My cellist was a wonderful-looking young chap with one of those compellingly beautiful Slavic faces. He'd been on the Russian front, been wounded, and, now, at all of seventeen, was mustered out and back to his music.

He spoke passable English and was immensely interested in America and American music, especially Aaron "Cooplund," as he called him.

I was charmed by him. I've always been a pushover for truly fine musicians, and he was excellent. I loved listening to his English. I loved watching his face as he sorted through the English words he had in his vocabulary to try and tell me what he was feeling.

I was thirty-five at the time, and being with someone seventeen gave me my first taste of being an "older man."

Despite what my studio bio said, I was not foreign-born, and this was my first trip out of America. Now that I look back on it, I realize that I was a babe, naïve as only Americans of that period were. Here I was out of America for the first time, having lived through a vast war I'd only seen in screening rooms. I felt displaced and alien over there—as I'd heard servicemen say they felt—and it made me achingly homesick.

My knowledge of Russia extended to conducting four scenes of Warners' *Mission to Moscow.* I had no idea what I was doing. I wanted comfort and affection from someone I was very attracted to, so I did something surpassingly dumb: I seduced my Russian friend. He wasn't inexperienced. He was gay, but we were in Russia.

He was lovely and I was very lonely and there was no way I could have known better. We made love three or four times at my hotel.

The day after our last time together, I noticed that he was missing from the orchestra. One of Alexandrov's assistants ran into me that day—not at all by accident, I felt sure—and informed me that my cellist friend had been unexpectedly found fit for active service at the front.

I should have known better. I really should.

After that, I spent my evenings with the Hollywood technicians.

It was spending time with the technicians that decided me to look into opening recording facilities in Hollywood. They talked about all the wonderful technological discoveries that would change sound after the war, about the things being done to produce high-quality sound. They were talking about what would be called high fidelity. And while we were at Mosfilm I saw a wire recorder they'd captured from the Germans. Of course, it was the granddaddy of tape recorders. A lot of things came together in my head, including the fact that I'd been hearing a lot about how important independent production would become after the war. Some intuition told me that I should pay attention to all this.

That's how I came to start my recording business, and that's what kept me solvent when I got blacklisted.

How do I feel about the war? . . . Don't clutter my story up with a lot of polemical nonsense. What difference does it make what I felt about the war? In sum, I felt we had to fight it, that's what I felt.

# Billy Hicks

The war changed my life, that's what it did. It changed all our lives. I got very bored with it after a while. Everyone did.

After the Germans fell, Americans just wanted to be done with the whole affair, because it didn't feel like war anymore. There were some bothersome shortages, and we had brownouts, and those silly Civil Defense people would run around in their awful metal hats, but otherwise it was more like some elaborate game we'd agreed to play and were heartily sick of.

I spent the last year or more planning for our life after the war, for Teddy and me.

After that terrifying Christmas Eve, Teddy changed, and I began to feel that we did have a future together. I don't think I would have been half as energetic about my planning if there hadn't been someone that I felt I could share my future with.

The fabric business Lily and I had started was now into manufacturing, and we were getting our first test runs of synthetic fabrics from Du Pont to experiment with. We knew we wouldn't be able to count on regular supplies of any natural fabrics except cotton for a long time after the war ended, and a huge demand for fabrics had built up over the years of shortages. Synthetics had a sensational future. Lily and I were going to be ready. And we started talking to the people who made wartime furniture about converting to peacetime manufacture. We planned to come out with a line that would be clearly different from prewar furniture. We guessed rightly that people would want a new look for a new era. It was a very hopeful time, and I loved being part of it.

Teddy had been to secretarial school and he could now be a real help to me.

I saw very little of the old crew through that last year of the war. Actually, it wasn't till the early fifties that we were thrown together again.

We came together again over that awful business about Carl and Wesley. It was awful, but I've always been grateful that it got us back together.

# Robert Regal

When I got kicked upstairs in the OPA I had less to do than before, and for a good deal more money. I could give a lot more time to managing the assets of the dozen or so clients I had by that time.

Financially, the war had produced substantial gains for all of us. These gains were modest measured against postwar projections. It was easy enough to figure out what would happen economically.

Demand for consumer goods would explode, so I bought the Generals. General Electric, which would find it easy to convert assembly lines back to manufacturing household products. I bought General Motors, although I knew conversion would take longer. But when cars started coming, there was five years of automotive deprivation to be made up for. I bought General Foods. All down the line, I bought where greatest consumer demand seemed indicated.

For myself, I planned to go back to study, and applied to the Harvard Business School the moment the situation looked propitious. A lot of servicemen from the best families would be returning there. It seemed worth investing some time to get to know them. I'd learned that much in Washington: Intelligence alone isn't enough. Also, there were courses in economics that were of great interest to me.

Yes, I knew the war was ending. I wouldn't miss Washington. "My general"? Nothing happened to him. That's the point of becoming a general.

Our affair lasted till late '44, when his wife decided she wanted him back for a few special services. She and I got along very well, and she was shameless in using my relationship with her husband to get free information on the market out of me. I'm

155

not sure my infrequent and rather hasty liaisons with her husband equaled the value of that information.

She was an ambitious lady. She preferred women, but if it would further her aims, she wasn't above the occasional heterosexual seduction. Of course she had to plan these in advance, they couldn't be done on the spur of the moment, because, as a rule, the lady wore army-issue khaki underwear. Her husband said it kept her in a permanent state of excitement. I was always grateful that he didn't wear what she wouldn't.

To put it plainly, she screwed him into an occupation post in France, and they moved there. That's when we ended our affair. She had her eye on an ambassadorship for him, and she finally got one.

He cried a lot when we parted. For my part, I was somewhat less moved. I did care for him, but apparently not as deeply.

It seems hard to believe I was only thirty-three then. But I felt old. I've always felt older. It seems that at any age, no matter what the possibility, I would think, "I'm too old for that." Now I am.

Even at thirty-three, I'd been through more than the sex seemed to be worth. I'd accepted that I had no choice but to be gay, that there was no alternative for me, no way out. But I knew I had options. I could pursue what seemed to me to be hopeless, or at least not worth all the effort, or I could give my energy and attention to getting something of what I wanted out of life.

Money has stood me in good stead. Even now, I can have what seems sexually sufficient with a phone call and a check. It serves the purpose.

Once one gets one's mind off one's crotch, it's amazing what one can do with one's life.

# Wesley Ober

I remember that I thought it odd at the time that just when the war got worst, most people seemed to lose interest in it. It got bloodiest and most awful just as people started organizing their lives around getting away from the whole thing. At least that was my impression.

That's probably because later in the war I got involved in organizing more shows for hospitals. I was seeing more and more young men pretty badly damaged while the papers and magazines seemed to be most concerned with getting back to peace.

America just seemed to get bored.

Maybe it's because the papers were full of what the world was going to be like in the future, which, at the latest, would be next week. I just wanted to get back to RKO. My big dream about peace was being in a Technicolor movie while I still looked like something.

The only real glimpse I got of the future was up in Schenectady, that awful place where Billy comes from.

Some general friend of mine had been an executive with General Electric. I'd never heard of the invention, but G.E. had actually introduced television before the war. I saw one of the sets. It looked like a mahogany mailbox and in the middle of it was this tiny screen about the size of a cocktail invitation.

G.E. was going to demonstrate television to a lot of Army brass for some reason or other, and the general arranged for me to take one of my small troupes of entertainers up and put on a show. I was supposed to direct and narrate.

I went up and put on the show, but I thought it was the dimmest piece of entertainment imaginable. I felt as if we were doing mime for the blind. The studio had only two cameras, and they were so big that they couldn't be moved, so the entertainers would have to move in front of them. I'd have the girls dance across the screen. They'd dance in one side and then out the other, because when they jammed themselves together to form a line in front of the camera, the picture was so crude you couldn't make out what was going on. You couldn't tell whether they were dancing or drowning. And a close-up of a head on the screen looked like a talking potato. I think it was a three-inch screen.

Worst of all, I saw myself on screen; the damned lenses added weight, and I looked like Sydney Greenstreet.

I told Robert about this television nonsense when I saw him in Washington. I remembered that he listened with great interest and tried to talk me into putting some money into the companies that held patents. I told him that no one in their right mind would sit in front of that fuzzy postage stamp when they could go to a movie theater and watch things that were bigger than life and in color. I'm glad I wasn't old enough to book passage on the *Titanic* when it sailed.

If Robert gives you a tip, you take it, even if he tells you to invest in a soybean farm on Forty-third Street.

I think the reason I disliked the awful little tube so much was because it made me look awful. Well, smarter heads than mine were wrong about it.

But I've grown very grateful for that dreary medium, and I'm meek as a lamb when the commercial director tells me to get out of my Dunhill suit and Gucci loafers and put on a cardigan sweater and trousers that sag at the crotch, put on an old, cracked voice and play a granddad who prefers Kool-Aid to Châteauneuf du Pape. Ah, those lovely residual checks. And all kinds of people stop me and say, "Don't I know you?"

I made one other unfortunate excursion near the end of the war. I was invited to do a cameo in a movie called *Lightning in the Land.* It was a supremely dreary item about Russian peasants, and I played a visiting commisar who gathers the folk in the square to tell them the Germans are just down the road and they'd better go load their hoes and turn their babushkas into slings. It was one day's work. I never did see the picture, but I hear that the villagers turned back a panzer division or two and completely routed the Hun. I can only imagine that the Germans were demoralized by the sight of the peasants and the quality of the production, guessing rightly that pillage wouldn't produce anything but cheap samovars, and rape would be an act of charity. It was an ugly piece of trash, but it had an awfully earnest script by an awfully earnest Communist screenwriter. Boy, did I get my ass in a sling over that one.

Anyway, teacher, that's how I spent my war. . . .

Robert said you'd asked him that question, and he said he had grave doubts about the state of your mind. My dear friend, wars don't *mean* anything. Maybe they mean that someone has something someone else wants. How's that?

I can tell you that the war gave me a great respect for my fellow performers. I watched them work under dreadful circumstances, belting out "Don't Sit Under the Apple Tree" with a bombardment counterpoint or doing *Hamlet* with jeep headlights for spots. But there are a lot of books to tell you about that.

The whole thing left me with wonderful memories. It left me feeling awfully good about what I was able to do. It also left me deeply sad when I'd hear of someone I knew getting kicked out for sucking a cock or two. It left me disheartened when some colonel I was sleeping with would tell me how well he was prosecuting some poor, gay dogface.

No, I never said anything. No one would, in those days.

I don't think there's anything I can tell you that will help you with what you want to do, help you understand what our war was like. It was a different world. Being gay was wrong. Everybody knew that, especially gay people.

## PART 7

---

# "When the Lights Go On Again (All Over the World)"*
## 1945–1950

*A song of the period that spoke yearningly of the better life the postwar era would bring.

When the atomic bombs struck Hiroshima and Nagasaki, the Second World War was brought to a quick and shuddering halt. The shock waves are still rippling out, but all that atomic technology meant to most people at the time was the surrender of the Japanese, some say a full year earlier than might have been possible otherwise.

Unlike conquering armies of the past, fifteen million Americans chose not to stay in service or overseas to engage in plunder, assure reparations, or even to occupy conquered countries. Americans were willing to settle for a few souvenirs and get home, these men and women brought immense pressure to bear on the government to return them home as quickly as possible. "Back to Home and Normalcy" could have been their slogan.

For a brief few years of war, the United States had been an active partner—an ally—in the international community opposed to Hitler, Mussolini, and Hirohito. However, once the "vicious Hun" and the "sneaky Nips" were conquered, most Americans considered the job done and wanted to dust off their hands and get back to normal, as if America's part in the war had been no more than the mother's task of breaking up a spat between the kids. All perfectly understandable: Historically, Americans wanted mainly to mind their own business. Here is how William Manchester viewed this moment in his *The Glory and the Dream:*

> In wartime the streams of history merge. Each of the republic's constituencies sees the struggle as a whole because everyone shares it and even participates in it, if

only vicariously. Afterwards the currents divide again. Insularity returns.

What did happen in the immediate postwar period was to set in cement many of the ways in which Americans would live in the coming decades. For instance, the thirties Depression and the war had reduced available housing to nil. Levittown and tract-house developments were the improvised, "temporary" answers to that severe postwar housing shortage. That improvisation was to strew Americans over the landscape in a *slurb* and forever (or so it seems) marry us to our automobiles. Concurrently, television was to pin us to our seats and alter entertainment, family relationships, society, and even our minds. In 1948 Kinsey was to publish what Noël Coward called his "deafening Report" and make the first public inroads into the Victorian/Puritan ethic. (It is not that Kinsey would redirect our sexual behaviors, it was that he would give us our first chance to be honest about them.)

Americans would have been quite happy to return to their radios, but television had been waiting and in 1946 a survey firm noted this about the few families that owned sets: 92.4 percent listened to less radio than before; 80.9 percent cut their moviegoing; 58.9 percent spent less time with books; 48.5 percent less with magazines. More than 70 percent reported an increase in visitors.

Besides TV, Americans had other new toys that would continue to amuse us. The first Polaroid cameras showed up in 1948 and the first LP record spun into view about that time.

Joseph C. Goulden wrote of that era in his book *The Best Years—1945-1950:*

In sum, America's interest in these, the best years, was distinctly escapist: four religious books, three books on a card-game fad (canasta), three books of humor [dominated 1949's best-seller lists]. Events beyond the individual American's control were gradually tugging him toward a share of a collective responsibility for the rest of the world. But he did not care to read about what this new obligation would require of him.

America's commitment to internationalism can be glimpsed in a headline that had parallels in other spheres. The headline read: "Survey Shows Nuremberg Trials Bore U.S. Public." As did foreign aid, the then-organizing UN, refugees, or anything "foreign." When you can't find a place to live, such concerns can seem remote abstractions.

The four men who speak in this book were no different from their fellow Americans.

Even the Kinsey Report (fully titled *Sexual Behavior in the Human Male*) was little more than the stuff of cocktail conversation for them. But some mention of the report's findings seems warranted, in that the changes in sexual self-regard that seem to have resulted touched those younger gay men with whom they would become associated in later years.

Again, some context is needed to help show the country's feelings about homosexuals. The year in which the Kinsey Report appeared was the same year in which Truman Capote's *Other Voices, Other Rooms* was published. *Time* magazine's review complained of the book that, despite whatever the book's virtues as literature, "the distasteful trappings of its homosexual theme overhang it like Spanish moss." That same year Gore Vidal's *The City and the Pillar* was also published. Many years later Vidal wrote in a new afterword to the book of what happened:

> When the book was published in 1948, it was received with shock and disbelief. How could that young war novelist turn into this? *The New York Times* refused to take advertising for the book, and most of the reviews were hostile. The press lectured me firmly on the delights of heterosexual love, while chiding the publishers for distributing such a lurid "memoir."

Those reviewers and social critics taking that high moral tone on both books must not have been among Kinsey's "one male in every three who had some adolescent homosexual experience," *or* among the ten percent of the male population that was "more or less exclusively homosexual" for at least three years between the ages of sixteen and fifty-five, *or* among the thirty-seven percent of the total male population that "has at least some overt homosexual experience to the point of orgasm between adolescence and old age." I would have loved to have been in the editors' offices as they sought out one-hundred-percent straight reviewers to chastise those two books.

Since two of our narrators were engaged in the movie industry, a word about the immediate postwar condition of that business seems needed, because moviemakers were completely unprepared for what was to happen to them in the postwar years.

In 1946 movie attendance peaked at eighty million admissions a week, topping even wartime records. It seemed to the studios that people were so enamored of movies *per se* that they would watch anything. But also, by the end of the war, movies cost twice as much to make as previously and unions were asking extraordinary money and benefits—and getting them. Then, for no apparent reason, attendance plummeted from 80 million weekly tickets in 1946 to 62 million in 1948, to about 27 million in 1950. Added to this, postwar income earned by American films abroad was often frozen in foreign countries, top Hollywood talent was starting to produce independent films, and, after years of government antitrust suits, the studios were finally divorced from their theaters in 1950. And all this says nothing of television, the eventually determining factor in the movie industry's future.

Thus, both Carl Mason and Wesley Ober returned to declining and altering industries.

Before returning to our subjects, one final note about the era may be helpful.

Although Communism was not an overwhelming domestic concern in 1945–50, public concern with the real and imagined threats of Communism increased during this period, as did anti-Communist sentiment. In early 1945, for example, seven out of ten Americans wanted to reward our Russian allies by sending them German men to help the U.S.S.R. rebuild its cities. By mid-1946 six out of ten Americans felt the Russians were organizing to dominate the world and one in four of those Americans were ready to go to war to stop them. By 1948 seventy percent of Americans viewed Russia unfavorably. The curve of rancorous feelings was rising in America and would peak in the moral devastation of McCarthyism. It seems ironic that one of our prime postwar distractions from world concerns —television—would be the medium McCarthy chose to rivet our attention to a "foreign menace."

It is of passing interest to note that both the issues of Communism and unionism combined in a 1945 Hollywood strike that became most violent at Carl Mason's studio, Warner

Brothers. On October 5 of that year, pickets massed at the Warner gates with stones, chains, bricks, and broken bottles and assaulted nonunion workers trying to enter the studio. Studio head Jack Warner watched from a studio roof in dismay, saying, "The revolution has come to Hollywood."

This is all by way of suggesting that the kindling for the new anti-Communist fire that singed Wesley Ober and Carl Mason in the fifties was laid a few years earlier. But in 1945 our narrators cared no more about such broader concerns than most Americans. These four men wanted a future that would be much like the past, only richer and better. Already "comfortable," Mason, Hicks, and Regal were to become wealthy, with status to match.

# Carl Mason

I remember my last day in Washington very well. It was April 12, 1945, the day President Roosevelt died. It was hotter than hell that day—and that night. I remember because I was working in an unventilated cutting room till three A.M. When I came out of the building, people were still up and about as if it were high noon.

There weren't many portable radios in those days, but every one of them in Washington was out on the street that night. All regular programs had been canceled, and there was nothing but interviews with Roosevelt's friends, and the only music was music they said he'd loved. They kept playing that dreadful "Home on the Range" and saying that it had been his favorite song. I couldn't imagine a man of his wit having a liking for that thoroughly banal pap. That awful song trailed me for days, all the way back to California. America couldn't seem to get enough mourning. It went on for days.

Roosevelt was dead, it was hot, and nobody wanted to sleep that night. Our President was dead. He was a kind of father to us. We'd elected him four times, so most of us grew up with him. Those who had loved him were out that night, and I was one of them, so I just trailed along to Lafayette Park where thousands had just gathered for an all-night vigil. I stood around for a while in the heat, sweating and crying along with everyone else. I didn't stay too long. I just wanted to pay my respects and I didn't want to be alone.

The next day I headed back to the Coast. I didn't know that I wouldn't come to Washington again for several years. I didn't leave with the feeling that I was free at last, though by that time I would have been very happy to be. The trip was just another lap in the shuttle I'd been running for years.

On May 8 Germany surrendered, and I could finally resign in good conscience from my civil-service appointment. The war-production group of the movie unit would be folding.

Warners wasn't caught flatfooted by the end of the war. They'd been preparing films geared to what they felt would be the postwar mood. My God, how wrong their guesses were.

We went on making movies as if television didn't exist. That wouldn't have been so bad, if we'd made wonderful movies. By and large we made prewar movies for postwar minds.

The word was out at most studios that employees would be looked on with disfavor if they were known to own a television set, or if they even alluded to the fact that such a thing even existed.

Now this will sound as crazy as it was. To get any television reception in those days, one needed a huge aerial. Something like that would have been a dead giveaway that your house harbored a television. So, if one were at all curious about TV, one had to go to a bar to see it. For most of us in the business this meant driving out to the hinterlands. One couldn't go just anywhere, for fear of being seen by some studio snitch, so secret sects formed and they would rush off to the oddest corners of L.A. to watch TV. It was our pornography.

I only went once, down to Laguna. I'd nothing against TV. What I couldn't stand was the sound quality. I still can't. One cannot squeeze a symphony orchestra into a three-inch speaker. Milton Berle fitted nicely.

The Depression had filled theaters and then the war went right on doing the same, only more so. And they'd sit through almost anything, and twice if it was in color.

After the war they'd be willing to sit in front of a TV with the same lack of discrimination. TV was full of the most appalling crap, but their crap was free, you didn't have to stir, and we charged seventy-five cents for things like *Janie Gets Married.*

I certainly didn't like most of what I was scoring. As you know, I never did get the studio's top properties, but what I was scoring after the war was awful, or maybe it just seemed that way.

Maybe it was because I'd had a chance to do first-class work on those war films, or maybe it was that I was thirty-five or so and growing up a bit, or maybe my childhood romance with movies was over. At all events, the movies I was working on seemed dim.

For my sins, I used to score a lot of movies made by a young actress of quite awesome insipidness. The critics' favorite word for her was "amateurish." They were of a kind bent. Dorothy Parker once said that Alice Faye had all the attraction of a big toe. Well, our ingenue was the big toe of a ballet dancer. Scores for her films were only slightly less demanding than the occasional work I'd do on a Bugs Bunny cartoon.

I started saving reviews of my movies after the war. If anyone wanted to trouble to find the origins of these quotes, they'd know who I was, but I can't think of a better way of explaining why I decided to get out of my contract.

I quote: "Harsh and unbelievable. The script is a frightful thing." . . . "Even with expert presentation, this would be an insufferable tale." . . . "A bleak indiscretion of Warners" . . . "As wretched a stew of picture-making as has been dished up in many a moon."

Some of those dogs have gained a kind of camp status, but in their time they did seem awful.

The studio's pictures weren't all dogs. Crawford came over from MGM and did some fine things. She made something called *Humoresque* for us which the critics loved, although I'd still like to know who told Miss Crawford the composer's name was pronounced "Show-pang." And we had Ida Lupino and Ann Sheridan. We made a few respectable things, but I wasn't assigned to them.

I'm very good at my job, and I didn't do a thing for three years that I could take any pride in.

If I'd been living up to my income, I'd have probably hung around. I would have had to. Unlike my compeers, I'd saved most of my earnings. I didn't care about having most of what Hollywood offered. Robert had done well for me in the market, and I'd moved all my investment work to him during the war.

I was *rather* rich then, which is why I decided to chuck in the studio work. That was in '48.

My decision was a long time coming, and when I did make it, I went to see Jack Warner before I said anything to anyone. I knew he'd have nothing better to offer me than what I'd been doing. The movie business was in trouble.

It was the last time I met with Jack Warner, and I remember it well. He'd been awfully good to me, and I wanted him to know that I knew that and appreciated it. I also wanted him to know how much respect I had for his talents. I remember that he settled in to talk with me like an old friend. He never seemed in a rush with me, he always seemed to have all the time in the world.

He told me a funny story about some trouble he'd had with the unions over who got to stuff the stars' bosoms. If the falsies were cloth, the costumers' union said they did the stuffing. If the falsies were foam rubber, the makeup union said they did the stuffing. Jack said it should have been the special effects department. Jack talked about a lot of things. I should have paid more attention to what he was saying about unions.

I told him that I'd pretty much made up my mind to ask him to release me from my contract. He said that he was very sorry to hear it, and he wished that he had some really wonderful movie to assign me to or some way to hold me, but he said that as things were going, they were going to have to start cutting back on their contract list. He said that even the best of his movies were having trouble finding an audience, and he wondered if he was losing his touch. I told him that I thought it was just that things were unsettled, were changing. He looked so pleased when I reminded him that he'd set the industry on its ear with sound, and that if there was any way of grabbing back the audience he'd find it. He did, of course.

He wanted to know what I planned on doing. I told him that I was thinking of laying off for a while, even doing some more studying. There was a remarkable teacher in England who taught vocal scoring, and I was thinking about going over to work with him for a year or so.

I didn't tell him I was thinking of setting up a recording operation to service independent producers. I thought that might hurt his feelings.

So we parted amicably. They didn't replace me. I was one of the first to leave. I'm happy I left under my own steam.

As you know, I've been back to work at Warners on the odd project. But it gets me down. I keep looking for the old faces. They're all gone. It's not like a family anymore.

I didn't know when I left that I'd been part of what they're now calling the Golden Age of Movies. That kind of thinking is sheer nonsense. The studio owned theaters it had to fill, and that's what all those movies were for. Not art, but product. If the damned movies look golden, it's because they had energy and vitality, something that's usually sorely lacking today.

The critics all wonder why a *Star Wars* made so much money. Just listen to the score of that movie. The damned thing is pure Max Steiner. When I heard it and saw the crawl vanishing in the distance, all I could think of was an old Errol Flynn epic. It was. If we'd had Dolby, we could have gotten that sound on the old lot, in the old studio. We had the talent. Indeed we did.

A few weeks after I left Warners I was on my way back East to talk with Robert about my idea of starting my own recording studio. I'd hired a nice young research student to compile a list of films scheduled for independent production, together with lists of the talent involved and the budgets they had. Then I had him call all these production officers and see what they planned to do about scoring and recording. I found out that they were almost all going to rent studio time and space for their scoring. And with studio overhead what it was, that was going to take a big chunk of their budget.

If I could offer producers the same music and sound services for even ten percent less, I was in business.

Robert and I worked together for two weeks on planning a start-up budget. I would have to take no more than half my net worth to get into business, and on a very decent scale. That still left me financially secure, so I was taking a minimal risk to get into what I was sure would be a highly profitable growth business.

None of this is very colorful stuff, but that is what I did after the war. I went after security. I know now that I also went after a way to stay in the movie business. That part of my life got less glamorous by the year, but then the business got less glamorous when the studios started slipping away to the money boys. As a friend of mine put it, we went from dreams to drachmas.

That may be sour grapes or old age—or both—but I'm always interested when I go to a revival of one of the old films and find the theater full of youngsters who seem as enthralled by a movie like *The Maltese Falcon* as I was when Adolph Deutsch asked me to come and have a look at it hot out of the lab. Just the two of us in the screening room. He was so tickled by what he'd done. He thought that his score had hit just the right mood. Pleased as punch with himself.

# Billy Hicks

See that brocade on the chair? Imagine, that was twenty dollars a yard in '52. I just ordered eighty yards of that at a hundred and ten dollars a yard, and that's *my* price. The blue cotton is seventy-five dollars a yard. And so on, and so on, and so on. I can't believe the prices. Maeve can afford it, but that's not the point.

I don't do many apartments myself any more, but Maeve's an old friend. She was one of my first clients, and she was a good friend to both Teddy and me. She's eighty-two and still going strong.

What else does a young man do? I was young and Washington had taught me that there was a lot more to be done with interior design than just fiddle with somebody's apartment. There were whole corporations that could use the kinds of things designers do.

Before the war we were interior decorators. People like me changed that, and now we're all interior *designers*. And, ducks, that's not at all like turning a garbage man into a sanitation engineer. Calling us designers was Lily's idea. She got it from David Selznick. I'm not sure David suggested it, but he'd created the term "production designer" to answer a nomenclature problem on *Gone With the Wind* and we picked up on it.

We all went out to make money after the war. That's what everybody did. Every American was going to be rich, and, good heavens, when you compare life today to what it was during the thirties, everybody is rich. Everybody has a phone, and a television, and a car, and strawberries twelve months a year.

By the time I left Washington, I was really rather weary of the place.

To get out of the service I had to have "points." But you could only get points for things like overseas duty, babies, campaigns. There were no points for decorating offices or putting up with generals' wives. The way the system worked, I'd have never gotten mustered out. So, I had to get out the way I got in: friends.

The day Germany surrendered, I started phoning friends, asking if they thought the army really needed me. Someone made some noise about sending me abroad to do something or other about officers' quarters in the occupied countries, and I almost took them up on it.

I would have gotten overseas and I'd never been. I had the feeling that there were a lot of goodies to be had, just sort of lying about. I thought better of it. How would I have gotten things back when they couldn't even get all the servicemen back?

But my friends finally pried me loose, and my Washington landlady called to say she was coming back. So I put the needlepoint swastikas back on her dining chairs and started packing.

By the time I got back to New York, they'd relit the city. All through the war there'd been something called a "brownout." All the lights in New York were dimmed or just turned out. I don't know whether that was to save electricity or to make it harder for bombers or what. But the place was in a kind of perpetual gloom.

The night I got home, Teddy and I went walking on Broadway, something I wouldn't dream of attempting today. It was about ten years since I'd arrived in New York. I'd been through a war and I was back, and there was Broadway just the way I remembered it. Glittering. Absolutely gorgeous, with the vast brilliant Wrigley sign bright enough to light five Schenectadys.

We had dinner at Toffenetti's. I can't remember what I had for lunch yesterday, but I remember looking out on Broadway and Forty-third, eating spaghetti, having pumpkin pie with whipped cream, being with Teddy.

# Robert Regal

I was mustered out of OPA by Chester Bowles himself. That was a signal honor. It was very nice to be given this kind of recognition by the director himself. He was the Bowles of Benton & Bowles.

I had been accepted at Harvard Business School. I would be taking courses in business law and some related to international trade. My faculty advisor said to allow three or four years for my doctorate. I planned two and a half. That's what it took.

While I was twiddling my thumbs waiting to get out of OPA, I managed to get a list of those accepted at the Harvard Business School. I did some research with that list. I estimated that the men in my class represented families that held strong controlling positions in corporations representing twenty-five percent of the gross national product. A formidable group.

I could have studied the subjects I chose at any number of schools and with less expense. Harvard would give me credentials. Harvard would give me cachet and contacts.

I had learned one thing in fourteen years of working for someone else. Most organizations are homophobic. That's the new word, isn't it? Like it or not, I was homosexual. I chose to minimize that disadvantage by creating a position of some power from which to do business.

When I reached Harvard I let it get around that I was divorced. In that era that was a social liability for a woman, but it recommended a man to hostesses when they needed a spare man.

With the connections I was able to make at school I was soon the spare man at some lovely Boston homes. I remember very vividly the first time I cabbed up Beacon Hill for a dinner party in Louisburg Square. I felt that it was the beginning of something better. I had covered the distance from Wilkes-Barre to Louisburg Square.

I was thirty-five. I was much more mature than my fellow students, but I brought to those parties a talent much admired by the men—business experience. And I was welcomed by those Boston women who were raised to prize stability in a man. Unlike the New York debutantes, the Boston virgin didn't expect to be ravaged for the sake of form. I was more comfortable in Boston than I have ever been in New York.

I was prototypical, if you will. There were few young men in America after the war who didn't pursue fortune. There was a lot of talk at the time about the number of men who joined the "52-20 club" and sat around on their ruptured ducks. Not most young men. America had either been poor or at war for almost a generation. We were finally going to be rich.

If my generation hadn't done what it did, yours would not have the luxury of living off that capital. It is likely that if America hadn't prospered, you would not be writing a book about a subject that in my time was not even discussed.

I had to survive in a different climate. I wanted to do more than survive. I wanted to prosper. I didn't want to go back to someplace like Price Waterhouse and know that without a wife and some statistical norm of children I could never hope to get anywhere, and I didn't want to go back to that demeaning, soul-grinding job I had before the war. I wanted the best. I'd taken my measure. Good or bad, I'd taken it, and if I couldn't have some things, I would have others. I would have some security, a say about my life. I'm grateful for what I have.

So reserve your judgment, or at least keep it to yourself.

All that my Harvard situation lacked was the requisite woman to squire about. So, I looked around and found Miriam.

Miriam was the sister of a chum of mine at school. She was a horsey girl, several years older than her brother, in her thirties when I met her. She dressed in the sturdy dowdiness of her class. I remember an endless number of sensible gabardine suits. I was often paired with Miriam at dinners. Primarily, I think, because of age, but undoubtedly also because she was marriageable and I, as an available man, might be more sensible about what I would look for in "another" wife. The idea of my sensibleness no doubt arose from the fact that I attributed my divorce to my former wife's frivolousness and spendthrift ways. Boston matrons usually disapproved of divorce, but not if it was necessary to protect capital.

Miriam was in the Eleanor Roosevelt mold. She was not shy, as I supposed, but vastly bored by most dinner conversation. With most women I avoided discussing business, because I could see their minds wander. I avoided business matters with Miriam until one evening I casually said something about some pending trade legislation I hoped would pass, and she said that the legislation was errant foolishness. She went on to tell me why, and we had the best conversation I'd had in ages—with a woman, that is.

After that, when asked to bring a companion to a party, I would ask Miriam. She liked me. We got along. We even had fun together. I even began to think that I might marry after all.

Miriam could be very appealing. She was a woman of warmth. She was also a woman of intelligence. The family's money would have been better spent sending Miriam to college, rather than her somewhat doltish brother. He never did better than C-minus or thereabouts.

Of course, after a while, matrons were asking rather pointedly about my intentions toward Miriam. I could honestly reply that I found her the best of company. Miriam, herself, never indicated any expectations beyond our companionship, so I let matters be.

Miriam's mother was dead; otherwise I would have been under some pressure. Miriam's father was a rather vague man who seemed disinterested in his daughter. I gather that he couldn't see any use for Miriam in the business, so that ended his interest in her. Besides, Miriam was so self-reliant that I suppose she made no demands. I know she didn't resent his disinterest.

But that kind of arrangement can never go on indefinitely. Something must happen. It did, of course.

After I had been at Harvard for a little more than a year—I had known Miriam for most of that time—I began to gather from matronly hints, to say nothing of hints from her brother, that I really must do something one way or another about Miriam. Miriam wasn't pressing, but I knew I must act fairly. And what, you might well ask, would be fair?

As nearly as my nature allowed, I loved Miriam. I took real pleasure in her company. She was not a foolish woman. She could talk sensibly about any number of things. All the makings of not only a nice romance, but of a sane alliance by Boston standards.

Also, I would fit most comfortably into her family's business. I admired her father's talents and could tolerate her brother.

All that passed through my mind. Then Teddy called and invited me down to New York for Thanksgiving. Teddy was back with Billy in their place on Park, and I'd sublet my New York apartment to a veteran. I won't go on at length about that weekend in New York, but when Teddy opened the door I knew more firmly than I ever had just what I was. There are no evasions possible when one loves someone as I loved Teddy. I'm a sensible man. I've never known why I couldn't let my feelings for Teddy die. I stayed with Billy and Teddy and watched them together. They never seemed right for one another, but there they were. They seemed to work around one another so easily. I try not to argue with facts. Teddy was a fact. I knew that weekend that I could no longer argue with myself about myself.

I didn't stay in New York as long as I'd planned. It was difficult for me to be around them. I made some excuse and went back to Boston early.

All the way back, I planned very carefully what I would say to Miriam. Unfortunately, I could not plan a way that wouldn't hurt her. It seemed clear that I should stop seeing her. I had no right to take up her time. It is not to my credit that my planning underestimated her.

When I knew what I would say, I thought about where we should meet and talk. I would be totally honest. I feared that she would cry. She didn't seem at all the kind of woman who would, but that's what I feared more than anything.

I remember that it was too cold to meet on the Commons, which I would have preferred, so I settled on a small tea shop on the Hill.

If she hadn't taken the bull by the horns, I'm sure I'd still be sitting there hemming and hawing, and mashing my napkin. She watched my discomfort as long as she could. She finally had to say . . .

I don't have Wesley's talent for drama, but I would like to try and get this correctly. First she told me to please stop fussing. Then she said, "You must know that I have never assumed you would marry me. I would have let you know I wanted marriage. We are the best of friends. I hope this won't hurt you, but I don't love you. I like you, because I like being treated like a person."

She said a lot of other things I can still remember. I've never loved a woman more than I loved Miriam at that moment. I have never trusted a woman more. I wanted to tell her I was homosexual, so there would be nothing less than absolute honesty between us. I finally did. Years later, I did. I think that speaks well of our friendship. When I told her, she said, "Boston would have been no place for you. I've always thought it killed my uncle."

We were both sensible back then. We continued to see a great deal of one another all the while I was at Harvard. People finally stopped talking about us and just accepted our arrangement as part of the social scenery.

About a year after I returned to New York, she wrote to tell me that a widower she knew had proposed and she had accepted, because she loved him. She even loved his three children. They had two of their own.

When each was born I took a hundred dollars and started a little account which I kept up till they were ready for Harvard. Over the years I'd made the accounts grow, and that bit of money ended up paying most of their school bills.

We've been the best of friends. About two years after her father died I took over her business affairs, but only after her brother started reducing them to a shambles. That man finally lost the family business. No easy job.

I hadn't thought of all that for years. . . . I've been talking entirely too long. I'm getting as verbose as Wesley, and tell him I said so.

I have never told anyone about all that, even the others. . . .

# Wesley Ober

We had an awful time getting some of our touring shows out of Europe when the war ended there. The minute the last shot was fired, everyone wanted to get home and forget the whole damned thing. So the USO people had to beg, borrow, and screw their way home. And there didn't seem to be much interest in beating the hell out of Japan. I knew, because I had a very hard time putting together shows for the Pacific. Everyone was tired. No one wanted to go to the Pacific. In the Pacific, the damp ruined everything, and people got these awful diseases.

All the stars who had flocked to go entertain troops were now very reluctant. Trouping was hard, a real hardship for the performers, and, God knows, they'd been generous to a fault. There wasn't anything for them in all that work, but they went and did a very tough job.

So, when things in Europe wound up and the steam just seemed to go out of the old engine, I started putting together scaled-down shows and sending out more packages of plays. The plays were one-set things with few actors, and they were easier to tour than the musical groups which had to have a lot of costumes and musicians and instruments.

When in doubt, we could always put together a package of a play called *Dear Ruth,* which always seemed to go down well, and didn't require the greatest talent, as we constantly proved. We had so many *Dear Ruth* troupes running around that we had to give them nicknames to tell them apart. The one with the dyke leading lady we called *Babe Ruth,* the one with the rapacious star we called *Dear Ruthless,* the one with the lisping star we called *Dear Wuth.* I bet we had twenty companies of that show. It was a little risqué for its time, and the men liked it.

As you know, things finally did end. I was very relieved. I was

183

tired. I was getting a little longer in the tooth and beginning to feel the grind. We wound things up in my department as fast as we could, but we completely lost track of one *Dear Ruth* company. We simply lost the file on them. For all I know they're still trouping in New Guinea.

I went back to RKO, under my old contract, which had simply been extended to the full seven-year term. Things looked terrific. Movie attendance actually went up right after the war, and all the studios thought it would just keep going up and up. All the foreign markets would open up again and we'd all just get richer and richer.

Well, for some reason, Americans just stopped going to the movies. Just stopped. They went from watching anything to watching nothing. The studios started this big campaign claiming that "Movies are better than ever," but all that produced was a ho-hum heard round the world.

I was again spending all my time on loanouts, and even did a role or two over at MGM, which was considered a real mark of distinction.

I played a veteran in one of those films. Americans were sure that all the servicemen would come home still kill-crazy after they'd tasted blood in battle. So, I was playing a paranoid veteran. It was a B picture, but at MGM that was still classy stuff. I played a veterinarian in the other picture I made for them, co-starring with a monstrous child and an incontinent canine. We figured out that the dog's trainer hated actors and kept the beast on a diet of figs. It was so bad that if we weren't in a long shot, we'd wrap our shoes in old rags. And the heat from those old klieg lights was no help. Ah, the glamour of movie-making.

I met Sheila at MGM, but that's getting ahead of myself.

I managed to ignore most of the signs that the business was falling in, and there were a lot. The studios—even MGM—were slashing their contract lists, budgets were being cut, free-lancers were setting up their own production outfits, using stars who had left the studios or been let go. Carl was even setting up his own shop. It didn't occur to me that if they didn't need stars, they wouldn't need supporting people like me.

My answer to impending doom was to buy a new house and take up with a very expensive young man who went right from wearing shoes on a regular basis to shopping at Cartier. The lad was a quick learner.

I even ignored two signs that would have dazzled a blind man.
I was being assigned roles on the Lux Radio Theater—a *radio*
show, mind you—and I was loaned to Monogram Pictures.

Even I knew radio was on its way out, so when I was put on a
radio show I felt the world was coming to an end. Radio! Lux
Radio Theater was a very classy show, in its way, in its time.
They even built a theater to house it. However, the idea of being
a disembodied voice after years of using all of me—so to
speak—was a drastic comedown. The signs were not good.

My loanout to Monogram really announced for whom the
bell tolls. Monogram Pictures, more commonly known as
Migraine Pictures, was the Woolworth's of moviemaking. I was
in a western of theirs shot in some awful new color process called
Agfacolor, which made the movie look as if it had been cast in a
hepatitis ward. The people looked yellow, the horses looked
blue, and the whole picture was so murky-looking that the only
way to tell the people from the horses was their color . . . except
when the heroine wore blue.

That western had a seven-day shooting schedule, undoubtedly because the glue factory wanted its horses back. That epic
was undoubtedly aimed at drive-ins, which were becoming all
the rage. I'm happy to say I never saw that movie and I have
never been in a drive-in.

All in all, I decided that I should cut back on expenses, and I
started by getting rid of my current lover, who merely packed all
the jewelry—his and mine—and left without a whimper.

But it never did pay to be less than extravagant in Hollywood,
so I bought a new Cadillac and started dating Sheila, my MGM
friend, and being seen everywhere it was worth being seen.

Of course, Sheila's companionship was not without price.
Sheila had to be screwed with regularity. I remember the first
night we were in bed and she got a death grip on my member.
She held it and tilted it hither and yon, examining it like a very
expert jeweler, and then said in the most reverent voice, "Now I
know how Moses felt when he got those tablets."

Madame was always telling the fan magazines that her life
might look glamorous, but fame exacted a terrible price, and
that she felt, to use her very word, "empty." That was her
favorite line: "I feel empty." Let me tell you, her life may have
been empty, but the rest of her was regularly full.

But she was only lugubrious when she was in her cups.
Otherwise she was good, funny company, and she had one of the

shrewdest business heads around. By MGM standards, she was a minor star, but she'd made it from silent movies to talkies where others had floundered, and year after year her fan mail stayed high. She had a nice range and could be used to add flavor to supporting roles in A pictures. In B pictures she was starred. Part of her glamour derived from having married two of the most desirable men in movies. How can I place her? She was a cut above Claire Trevor but a cut below Lana Turner. She was somewhere around Mary Astor.

Like me, she was getting to be "of an age," as they say. But when MGM let her contract lapse, she didn't go the route of a lot of the stars who were suddenly out in the cold world to scrape parts where they could. The lady sat herself down with her business manager and agent and looked at the facts. No panic for her. She knew she had a name and some talent, and she planned to get the most out of both.

She looked at what she could earn doing one or two films a year, and she looked at the other stars who were battling for even second-rate stuff at such joints as Universal and Columbia. She decided that wasn't for her.

She figured that she could make more by packaging her own touring productions of plays, and controlling her own expenses and casts. And she liked to work. She said that it wasn't just doing lousy roles that bothered her, it was all the waiting around between pictures.

We were good friends. She knew about my gentlemen friends and, having had a few ladies in her day, it didn't bother her one way or the other. So, when she decided to hit the road, she invited me to go along. I had just finished my ninth Lux Radio Theater and my Monogram movie, so I said yes. They were first-class tours, with long playing times in major cities.

RKO was glad to let me out of my contract. They hadn't been making a profit on my loanouts for a long time, so off Sheila and I went in an appalling play that audiences loved.

Even the play was commissioned by Sheila for a set price to the author. She owned the whole shooting match.

The play had only one set, but Sheila had ordered the play broken into as many scenes as possible, and each scene was the occasion for a costume change for her. There were seventeen scenes. She limited herself to only six wigs.

We tried out in Baltimore. One particularly affronted critic said the show wasn't so much dramatic as emetic. (I've always rather liked that line.)

But we packed them in. Grandmothers would climb on top of cars to get a look at the lady when she exited the theater. Every day was like a fire sale at the stage door. Hordes of elderly women rioting. And Sheila would give them a show. She had several costumes she wore just from the stage door to the Rolls that was always waiting for her. She was like the Queen Mum, but a helluva lot better dressed.

I couldn't believe the business. And I felt lucky. I was lucky. I was starring in a piece of nonsense that would do very good things for my career.

A lot of the script didn't even make much sense. Sheila played a widow with a young son who was determined that his mother and I would not marry. I had one speech that I still remember, because I had such an awful time learning it! In the second act I said to Sheila, "And when do you have a life of your own that allows my love to enrich the days we may yet share even with your son despite loving us both." I've always felt the typist just left out a line. I said the line very ardently—not that it mattered. All through it Madame was busily arranging several acres of heliotrope marabou.

Sheila knew her audience, and decided to use more than just my thespian talents. She told me that under no circumstances was I to wear underwear on stage. I argued about that. Cheap stuff, I said. You see, in my day, movie actors who were featured were bound up, and under no circumstances was there to be any indication of one's endowments. That kind of thing was all right for bit players and chorus boys, but not featured players. Sheila was adamant. As she said, "Honey, you show or no show." She was right. A lot of old dears were literally on the edge of their seats and not averse to using opera glasses, even in the orchestra. And we never had an empty seat down front. I was years ahead of Tom Jones.

No matter where we booked, we ended up staying months longer or booking a return engagement.

Art's all well and good, but I've never seen anything wrong in giving the audience something it likes. And they liked us.

Can you believe that I spent six years trouping in that?

I didn't see much of the old gang during those years. It wasn't like today, when you can hop a plane in the morning and be anywhere in a few hours. It was a couple of days from New York to Chicago. But Teddy was a good letter writer and kept me up to date. His letters got more and more like the financial pages. All my old friends were getting rich, and Teddy'd report their affluence.

All in all, I was happy to be away from Hollywood. Not only was business off, but there was all that mess about the Communists. I felt well out of the whole thing.

I'd get letters from jittery friends telling me how awful things were out there, about loyalty oaths and blacklists and bad movies. I knew a lot about what was going on, because I did follow *Daily Variety*. I even read the daily papers when that Rankin man went after some people I knew.

I know it was all some time in the late forties, but I'm not sure about exactly when. This Rankin person was a congressman or something, and he decided he was going to get the Communists out of Hollywood. In those days, the name of Hollywood could still get a lot of publicity. So this Rankin decided to get the Reds out of Hollywood. And he got lots of help. Peculiar help, but lots of it. Ronald Reagan testified about how the Communists were writing all the movies. And Adolphe Menjou did the same, and George Murphy. My favorite witness was Ginger Rogers's mother, Lela. If I remember correctly, she said she wouldn't let her Ginger play the lead in the film version of *Sister Carrie*, because Dreiser's book was Communist propaganda. When I'm gloomy I think about Ginger Rogers as Sister Carrie and it perks me right up.

But it wasn't funny. Some wonderful people were completely destroyed. Good writers were out on their ass—people like Ring Lardner, Jr., and Dalton Trumbo—and they either ran away or had to make a living writing under assumed names. The people that investigation hurt couldn't make a living at their trade.

I actually got a letter from an old actor friend who had ended up working as a part-time gardener. Can you imagine?

And there I was on the road with Sheila, secure, well paid, and, as it turned out, living in a fool's paradise.

# Carl Mason

For me, the songs of the late forties signaled the fall of civilization. We had such musical confusion as "Chicery-Chick," "Mairzy Doats," "Rag Mop," and "Hutsut Ralson." It was played everywhere on those awful jukeboxes. At all events, the Vandals had breached the gates, and it was all downhill to a song I heard recently which had a lyric that simply said over and over that it was all right to fuck all night and suck all day. No, I didn't like the music of that time.

But then I was beginning to be able to do some good work at my own recording studio. Once the decision was made to do it, the project went along like a house afire. Robert advised me to take on two limited partners, one to manage the business end and one to be in charge of the technical work. I hired two gay friends, one from Universal and one from Decca Records. I'd like to say that I did that in the spirit of gay unity, but they were the only two competent people willing to risk leaving steady work. We worked well together, and, as things turned out in the fifties, I was very happy I'd organized things that way. There was someone to take charge when I ran away.

What I hadn't planned on when I went into business for myself was the unions, and particularly a gangsterish fellow named James Caesar Petrillo. Petrillo headed the musicians' union, and after the war he started making life hell for everyone who employed musicians, particularly the movies. Can you believe that he was trying to get musicians' hours down to ten a week, and he didn't want them to work more than two minutes in any hour? Absurd! Very obviously he was not himself a musician and even referred to people who played winds and reeds and tympany as "those people who play horns and bang drums."

My real trouble came from trying to hire the best musicians I could get for the first score I was hired to produce and record.

I'd been lucky and had gotten the job of scoring a first-class independent production. I was to write the score, and my company would record it and do all the work on the track. It was a good start, a good omen. I was going to work on an A picture, and I would not have to work my way up as I'd feared. I never did have to score any more dross, but our tech people would work on anything, industrial films, filmstrips.

Getting the best musicians was a chore. I could have picked up a lot of studio men to moonlight, but that wouldn't work with our schedule, and if a musician got stuck doing overtime at the studio, I'd have been out of luck. I couldn't chance it.

So I lined up a lot of foreign musicians and spent days auditioning and putting together an orchestra. Naïvely, it never occurred to me to ask any of them if they had union cards.

Just as I finished assembling my orchestra, Petrillo went on a rampage to drive all the foreign musicians out of the business.

Petrillo always had his people snooping about the studio, and he also had spies, usually shop stewards who interpreted work rules the way Calvin interpreted the Bible.

I had my orchestra waiting to be called, but, considering the climate in Hollywood, I was afraid to use it. Almost all American unions were on a rampage at the time. Strikes everywhere, and over anything. Using an all-foreign orchestra suddenly seemed dangerous; that could get my client's movie picketed from coast to coast.

There was a pleasant German cellist I'd hired who kept dropping by the office to see me on any pretext. He was good-looking enough, and I thought, You don't have to put out to work for me. He was a fine musician, that was always enough for me.

I wasn't at all interested in him. I rather resented his thinking I would take advantage of my position, and I didn't think much of him for offering himself. It didn't occur to me that he simply liked me. Of course I hadn't been without sex since Jimmy, as you know, but I didn't want anything more than sex.

After all, I was thirty-eight. I'd loved Jimmy and didn't want to go through all that again. I just wanted to stick to what worked for me and stay safe. No more high drama, thank you.

I didn't miss Jimmy anymore. Not that I didn't play "what if" in my head about us. (What if I'd talked him out of going? What if he'd lived?) I couldn't bring myself to encourage anyone else. I had a great deal of what I wanted out of life, and I've never been greedy.

Frederich, my cellist friend, stopped by one afternoon, unannounced, and I was in no mood for a little chat, and much less for making goo-goo eyes. My union problem was on top of me. I almost threw him out. I certainly wasn't courteous. He wanted to know what the matter was, so I told him.

He listened and, when I was done, merely smiled and said, "Bwibewy." I started laughing, because he couldn't have picked a more unlikely word to use his fractured pronunciation on. I found it so funny that I didn't let on I'd understood and said, "What?"

And he said, "Bwibewy! Bwibewy!" which really set me off.

He didn't expect to be laughed at, but he finally got the joke.

He said something like, "My English may be faulty, but not as faulty as your thinking." Then he chose his next words to avoid his pronunciation traps and said, "Pay some union people off."

Then he got up, looking the picture of pained dignity. He told me, "Now that I've given you some advice and a good laugh at my expense, I'll leave. I will not play in your orchestra. I think there is a meanness in you. I don't like that, and if I had my cello with me I would shove it up your ass." That was clear enough, and out he went.

I paid some people off, and several heads were averted. All we had to do was record between 10 P.M. and 7 A.M. My "phantom" orchestra performed beautifully. The movie won me my first Academy nomination.

I remember the scene with Frederich well, because we've both told that story often enough over the years. I sent him flowers, a thank-you note for his advice, and an invitation to dine with me.

I rarely went out in public, but I knew that Frederich had been living on short rations, and I wanted to make up for what he must have felt was a very cruel joke at his expense, so I took him to the Beverly Hills Hotel for dinner.

I sat in the restaurant downing martinis at a great clip, while he sipped at his first glass of wine. He asked me if I always drank that much, and I said that I was trying to get drunk enough to make a pass at him.

He said that if I got drunk he wouldn't get to know me, and, besides, he didn't go to bed with drunken gentlemen. I've never really been sure how he turned me into the pursuer. It probably wouldn't have lasted if I hadn't felt it was *I* who'd won him.

Considering that all I ever really wanted out of life was working with music, life has been very good to me.

Oh, yes, there have been many problems, but I've weathered them: McCarthy . . . exile . . . even disco music.

# Billy Hicks

What weren't we into?

Within three years, Lily and I had made Continental Fabrics a national organization, our furniture company was overwhelmed with orders even though we were offering nine months' delivery, and our contract business for corporations was taking off.

I had a spiel I used when I pitched a new corporation about designing their entire building. I didn't just sell furniture and fabrics and design, I sold an idea. I'd tell the assembled executives, "Pharaohs built pyramids, the Church cathedrals, and the dominant cultural and social force of our time, the corporation, is building towers that are perfect reflections of a vigorous, high-technology society. The interiors of these 'machines' for modern working man should reflect that modernity and vigor." Have you ever heard such highfalutin' crap? It was the old medicine show, love. But that's the kind of stuff that took us from doing one twenty-thousand-dollar apartment to doing a whole new building for twenty million. The sales of snake oil were high those years. Still are, if you've got a good pitch.

And things were calm on the home front, for which I was grateful. Oh, Teddy would go on the occasional toot. That was messy, but bearable. It wasn't a daily thing. He went back to his old heavy spending, but I could afford almost anything that took his fancy. I was happy with the way things were between us. The others weren't, but I was. Besides, what Teddy did was really none of their goddamned business. That, I might add, had never stopped them from minding my business.

Wesley was bad, but Robert was the worst. I was designing Robert's new offices on Park and he wouldn't let me alone about

Teddy. "Aren't you worried about him? Do you intend to just let him go down the drain?" Teddy was no problem and if he was, he was my problem.

# Robert Regal

I was in a position to go into business in a very respectable way after I left Harvard. I was setting up a personal financial consultancy. Billy and Carl were already substantial accounts, and since my time in Washington I numbered three senators and two generals among my clients. Those few clients alone would justify an appropriate setting for the business. To begin I would have a lawyer and CPA on staff, then would hire research and other people as I needed them.

Billy said he would personally design my offices, and at cost. But what a cost. I am not, nor was I, General Motors.

I never won a single argument with Billy about the way the offices would look. When he was all done, my clients were duly impressed, so I assume he was right. With a vast amount of my money he was right.

He was not right about Teddy. He didn't seem to mind that Teddy was only going on occasional binges, two or three or so a month. What Billy refused to notice was that two or three were all Teddy could manage, because after each one Teddy would be too debilitated to drink again for a while. Billy never saw the real aftermath. Teddy would come over to my place when the withdrawal was worst. He'd have the DT's at my apartment. Have you ever seen someone experience them? They stare at nothing and scream at it. I'd take him to Bellevue when they would get too dreadful or I'd see the convulsions starting. I became astute at measuring the degree of emergency. But, as Billy said, Teddy only drank now and then.

I know I should have minded my own business, and my calling makes me unusually suited to doing just that. However, the discretion appropriate to fiscal matters did not seem applicable. Teddy was failing. That prognosis was not surmise on my part, that is what the doctors were telling me.

The last time I hospitalized Teddy was the worst. Until that time, I'd been able to get Teddy to the hospital in a cab. That last time I called an ambulance. In the past he had shaken or screamed; that last time, he would curl into a tight ball and then his body would suddenly shoot straight and rigid. That last time, he didn't scream, he just stared at something I was happy I couldn't see. Clearly, an ambulance was needed.

After the doctor had finished sedating Teddy he talked to me. He asked me if I was a member of the family and I said yes. He said that I had better get Teddy to stop drinking or—and he was blunt—Teddy would be dead. One binge more, maybe two, and his liver would just be gone. That was plain enough.

I checked several sources to find out what kind of help was available for Teddy's problem. I must admit I hated doing it. Anyone who starts a sentence with, "I have this friend who has this problem . . ." is automatically suspect himself.

The best I could seem to do was Alcoholics Anonymous. I must say, they didn't sound very promising. I asked what they did to keep people sober and all they kept saying was "meetings." I asked what their recovery rate was and they told me they had no idea. They kept no records. I asked what they charged, and they said nothing. Experience told me that what you get for nothing is nothing. However, I couldn't find anything else that anyone could tell me held promise.

Teddy and I had never argued heatedly. We did over his going to one of those Alcoholics Anonymous meetings. Teddy didn't want to stop drinking. I told him that if he didn't at least go, I would no longer be able to see him, I could no longer open my home to him. He would have to come off his drunks at home or wherever he could find. Not to make a pun, he found that sobering. I had never been that firm with him.

After a very long and very disagreeable discussion, Teddy agreed to go to one of those AA meetings, but only if I would go along.

I'm not given to overstatement, but I must say I found the whole experience macabre. The meeting was in a church basement.

I think one has to go to one of their meetings to understand what goes on. I'll describe what I remember, for what it's worth.

The church we went to was on the Upper East Side. We got

there early, because I got the hospital to hold on to Teddy till near the time of the meeting, so that I could take him right from there to the meeting. This precluded his having a drink.

When we went into the basement room there was only one man there, fussing with a coffeepot. I looked around for some place to sign in, but didn't see any, so we just went and sat down. The room was arranged like a theater, with just a table and chair facing the audience. A most unpromising setting.

The place finally filled up, and I was very relieved to see that the people seemed rather ordinary and quite well dressed. I was most surprised to see women there. I also found it curious that they were all sober.

The biggest surprise was what they called "the speaker." The speaker was a very well-turned-out woman who proceeded to tell the most awful stories about her drinking. The more gruesome her stories, the harder the people there would laugh. One hilarious vignette had to do with her urinating on her hostess's rug. That story caused the greatest amusement. I thought that nice people didn't talk about those things. I, for one, wish they wouldn't. I concluded that the reason they'd all stopped drinking was that they'd gone stark raving mad.

Teddy sat on the edge of his chair, like a child hearing some particularly fascinating story. I heard him laugh along with the others at every horrid tidbit.

They had an intermission and someone started talking about money, and I thought, Ah, here's the pitch. When the basket they passed came to me, I noticed it was filled with only coins. They weren't going to be able to do much with that. Things looked dimmer to me all the time.

When the people got up to get coffee, a man came over to Teddy and asked him, before he could ask me, if we were new to the group. I quickly informed the man that I was merely Teddy's friend. After some talk he took Teddy off to meet the others. I didn't see any point in my being involved and, frankly, they made me nervous.

When it was all over, Teddy and I left, and I walked him home. I was sure the evening was a waste

I didn't know what to say, because i couldn't see how that lot with their awful tales and all that "identifying" they talked about could possibly help Teddy. All I could think was that Teddy would drink again and he would die.

I have never been disturbed by the idea of death. The way

Teddy would likely die did disturb me, because I believed it would be too terrible for me to be near. I was ready to tell Teddy that I would never be able to see him again.

Making such a statement struck me as being in the realm of the dramatic, but I couldn't bring myself to watch the end.

Teddy hadn't said a word for blocks. About a block from his apartment he told me that he thought he was going to be all right, that he planned to go back to AA the next day. He completely startled me by asking me to pray for him. I told him, honestly, that I didn't pray anymore, but that I would do as he asked. I found it a most surprising request. It was very unlike Teddy. I thought that their madness must be catching, that Teddy might be sober, but he'd be mad. I regretted taking him to that meeting.

He did keep going back to AA. I'd seen quite enough of them that one time. He stayed sober.

Billy was irritated that Teddy was out all the time at those meetings he went to. Billy complained to me about it and I'm afraid that I snapped, "Would you rather see him dead?" That ended that conversation.

Months later I got home to find my apartment filled with flowers. I mean that there were dozens upon dozens of all kinds of flowers. Teddy had put them there. He'd also left a card that said something about it being his first full year sober—his "anniversary," he called it—and that there was no way he could thank me for his life or the first self-esteem he had ever known. He told me I was very important to him and that he loved me.

I knew that.

# Wesley Ober

Teddy wrote me about his joining AA, and I couldn't make head or tail out of what he was talking about. It seemed to work for him, so that was good enough.

My life was of a piece. Our tour had taken on a comfortable rhythm and we stayed long enough in each place for me to take a service flat and make some friends, and even have an affair or two. But the road does play havoc with the waistline, and I was beginning to have to pay some attention to mine. When it got out of hand, Sheila would take to patting me on the stomach and murmuring, "We'll call him Bill." That was my cue to diet.

How lulling it all was. I forgot Hollywood, and I only went to a movie if an old friend was in it, so I could write and say how much I enjoyed his or her performance.

On we sailed. I can't seem to remember much of that period in any detail. We rose late, lunched, rested, played, and stayed up partying after the show.

The only thing I remember vividly is my forty-fifth birthday. Sheila had had hers, but she had scattered so many birth years in biographies that no one was sure how old she was. I might have overlooked that birthday, if some smart-ass hadn't sent me a card that said, "You're either two twenty-three-year-olds or half a nonagenarian." After I looked the word up, I went into a complete funk, and took to paying very close attention to my elbows and behind. That's where age grabs you, young man, your elbows and behind. Still, for some reason, it was the first birthday I really paid attention to. I felt there was a message in the event, and I didn't like it. An actor's age is an actor's roles. I only knew how to be a leading man.

But as I say, that whole period was rather dreamlike. Nothing about Sheila or the show inspired any sense of reality.

I lived in a fool's paradise. Mind you, I have nothing against paradise, foolish or not, but when reality hits, the shock can be terrible.

Now, to understand this next bit, you must think of me clutching a bomb, hatching plots in cellars, consorting with Peter Lorre in dingy Viennese restaurants, and planning to overthrow the government. Hah! But that was the next role I was scheduled to play.

# PART 8

---

# "The Red Blues"*
## 1953

*A satirical song by Cole Porter, written for the movie version of his stage musical **Silk Stockings**.

Stories of America's anti-Communist purges of the late forties and early fifties are still told in a tone both horrified and aghast. Though people in all walks of life and of all sexual persuasions were affected by the anti-Communist witch-hunts, for the purposes of this book I have restricted my background sketch of the purges to the entertainment industry and to how it affected gay people.

So destructively pervasive was the effect of Senator Joseph Raymond McCarthy on the American scene that his name lent itself to the term "McCarthyism," which the Random House Dictionary defines as:

1. Public accusation of disloyalty to one's country, esp. through pro-Communist activity, in many instances unsupported by proof, based on slight, doubtful, or irrelevant evidence.
2. Unfairness in investigative technique.

McCarthy's legislative vehicle for carrying him to national prominence was the House Committee on Un-American Activities (HCUA), an inquisitionlike Congressional committee already sullied in reputation by its past chairmen, Martin Dies in the thirties and John Rankin in the forties. It was Rankin who rummaged through Hollywood's talent to unearth the group that came to be called the "Hollywood Ten," primarily a group of screenwriters with tenuous but provable links to the Communist Party.

The fuel that powered HCUA was a mixture of America's postwar disaffection with the Russians, its prewar distrust of

Communism revivified, a rampant "America first" attitude that masked an underlying isolationism, and, though less touted, anti-Semitism, political and corporate antiunionism, and the real or imagined links between unions and organized crime. A heady brew of mixed motives, to which was added the chance for the unscrupulous to earn large profits and power from joining the anti-Communist ranks.

Excellent writers who have since addressed themselves to unraveling this era are never wholly successful, because they are trying to make intelligible a national spasm that is inherently mad. But perhaps the following events will convey something of the temper of those times:

- In 1944, studio heads who were the main movers behind the powerful Motion Picture Alliance hired Ayn Rand to provide do's and don'ts for movie producers. She wrote, "Don't smear the free-enterprise system; don't deify the common man; don't glorify the collective; don't smear success; don't smear industrialists."
- As to the verification of culpability, many claimed to have sure-fire systems of identification: Adolphe Menjou claimed anyone who applauded Paul Robeson's Communist songs was a Red; screenwriter Rupert Hughes claimed he could "smell them"; the previously mentioned Lela Rogers cited as tainted the movie *None But the Lonely Heart,* with its "despair and hopelessness" and its background music by the immigrant German Communist Hanns Eisler, which was, in her words, "moody and somber throughout, in the Russian manner." Wise heads in HCUA were solemn in their acceptance of such help and grateful for guidance.
- To "protect" businessmen from unknowingly hiring "Communists," three former FBI men formed American Business Consultants. For a fee, ABC would "clear" people and verify their "loyalty." Consulting firms like ABC might advise an ad agency, for example, that they could provide a dossier on a "Commie actress" for $1,000. If the ad agency declined to buy, the agency's client would be attacked publicly for hiring a "fellow traveler."
- The American Legion was avid and hyperactive in their pursuit of the smeared, urging the organization of letter-writing groups to "phone, telegraph, or write to

radio and television sponsors employing entertainers with known front records." ("Front" was the short form of "Communist Front.")

• In an effort to help their fellow professionals, Hollywood's famous came out against HCUA. Among their number were Gene Kelly, Humphrey Bogart, Judy Garland, Katharine Hepburn, and directors John Huston and William Wyler. Jittery studio heads discouraged their efforts: For example, in Hepburn's case, Louis B. Mayer informed her that he could not use her in a movie again until she became publicly acceptable. All the above people were ruthlessly pressured to recant and then shut up.

• Jack L. Warner, Carl Mason's former employer, publicly pledged that he and his brothers would contribute to a fund to "ship to Russia the people who don't like our American system of government."

The above only suggests the dimensions of what was going on. "Red-baiting," as it was known, was going on in every sector of American life, and was spread cancerously by the aptly named "blacklist." Blacklists were compiled from casts of shows, which the likes of Lela Rogers and Adolphe Menjou deemed pro-Communist, from lists of donors who gave their name or money to "suspect" groups or causes, from informers with grudges, from those who stood to profit from the downfall of another, from gossip. Even misspelling could add the unwary to a list. (Jim John, John Jensen, J. Jimson, it was all the same to the fevered compilers of lists that were, most importantly, lists *for sale*. The more names, the more profitable the list.) And the list compilers stole from one another, perpetuating and multiplying damage. Blacklists became a kind of demonic chain letter. However, it needn't all be written down: a whisper would do.

Those called to appear before HCUA represent only a tiny fraction of the total number victimized by blacklisting.

The pursuers were often frank in saying that, to be sure, some innocents would fall before the attack, but what were the lives of those hapless few when measured against an untainted America?

The last intensive HCUA investigation—this one under McCarthy's leadership—began on March 8, 1951. In that year some thirty Hollywood ex-Communists named some three hundred colleagues. The studios panicked, because it further endangered the financially ailing movie industry. Again beseiged by HCUA, Hollywood was in a mood to capitulate, and with dispatch. When MGM learned that an actor appearing in their production of *Julius Caesar* had shown up on a blacklist, he was called off the set still wearing his toga, fired on the spot, and ordered off the lot—and completely out of his career, as it turned out.

So, as long as there was a broadly supported national purge underway, the "purifiers" also went after other groups of undesirables. The extent of the allied purifications is suggested by a comment by Senator Wherry, a onetime mortician and tractor salesman, who opposed any social legislation as "thinly disguised handouts" and who thought anyone who worked for the State Department was "Communist, homosexual, or Anglophile." The previously mentioned Wherry wanted to "get rid of the alien-minded radicals and moral perverts in this administration." David Caute says in his book, *The Great Fear*: "The enemies of [President Roosevelt's] New Deal depicted the State Department . . . as a veritable nest of Communists, fellow travelers, homosexuals, effete Ivy League intellectuals, and traitors."

As often happens, gay people were again appearing on the shopping lists of the moral hounds, this time as being synonymous with Communists.

The unfounded commingling of Communists and homosexuals in the public mind resulted undoubtedly from such blatant and unsubstantiated nonsense as this excerpt from the chapter called "Garden of Pansies" in Jack Lait and Lee Mortimer's 1951 book, *Washington Confidential*:

> The good people shook their heads in disbelief with the revelation that more than 90 twisted twerps in trousers had been swished out of the State Department. Fly commentators seized on it for gags about fags, whimsey with overtones of Kinsey and the odor of lavender. We pursued the subject and found that there are at least 6,000 homosexuals on the government payroll, most of them known, and these comprise only a fraction of the total of their kind in the city. . . .

When asked about "deviates in government service," FBI Director J. Edgar Hoover estimated a much more modest 406. The tone of Lait and Mortimer is not unusual for the period.

The Republican National Chairman, Guy G. Gabrielson, said in 1950: "Perhaps as dangerous as the actual Communists are the sexual perverts who have infiltrated our government in recent years." Perhaps better than anyone, Senator Wherry voiced the generally confused and invidious thinking in his comments during an interview with columnist Max Lerner that same year: "You can't hardly separate homosexuals from subversives. Mind you, I don't say every homosexual is a subversive, and I don't say every subversive is a homosexual. But a man of low morality is a menace in the government, whatever he is, and they are all tied up together."

To that, the thoughtful reader might well reply, "Huh?"

But, like it or not, gays were again thrown in for good measure when there seemed to be a shortage of good Christians for this Circus Maximus. America was going to be purified or a lot of people would know the reason why.

When it came the turn of Carl Mason and Wesley Ober, they stood in double jeopardy, having been labeled as both homosexuals and Communists. If trapped, they would be doubly tasty to the ravening appetite of the McCarthy committee.

# Carl Mason

Every time I answered the phone at home, I heard this clicking noise, and I would have trouble hearing whoever called and they could barely hear me. I suppose wiretaps were a good deal more crude in those days than they are now.

I called the phone company and complained, and they called back and said they couldn't find any trouble on my line. I would have just passed the matter by if I hadn't been talking to Wesley in Chicago or wherever his show was. When he answered his phone, I heard a click, and when he said hello I heard another click. We could barely hear one another. Apparently two wiretaps suck up almost all the sound.

We were yelling at one another and we could still barely hear, so we hung up and had the operator try another connection. Again, click and click. We had another bad connection, but I heard Wesley yell, "I think it's my phone. I can barely hear people these days."

What did I know about wiretapping in 1953? It was unheard-of. I was an American citizen in America. It just never occurred to me. It would today. It would to a lot of people.

The whole awful possibility began to dawn around May of that year when a pair of FBI men came to my office asking about one of the musicians I'd been using, an oboist.

Those men are frightening. The name of the FBI was unsettling, because it was linked in my mind with the most awful criminals. When they called, I could only wonder, My God, what have I done?

They had dead eyes and no expression. No matter what one said to them, it just seemed to sit in the air. They just didn't respond. They asked me questions about the musician, and it never occurred to me not to answer. They didn't say why they wanted to know, and I was too intimidated to ask. It never occurred to me to call my lawyer or that I even had a right not to answer. How long had I known this musician? Had we any relationship other than business? Did I know anything of the man's personal life—or habits or political inclinations or his home life? I wanted to answer, "No, why should I?" but they frightened me.

They questioned me for over an hour. I sweated. Near the end, they asked me to keep in touch with their L.A. office and to make some effort to learn more about the man. I was to keep in touch with them. If I didn't call them, they'd call me.

Just as they were at the door to leave, one of them said, "Maybe that friend of yours, that Stosser, could find something out. They're both Germans." His voice put "that friend of yours" in quotes, and there was a sneer in the man's voice. The other one gave him a dirty look. That was the first human expression I'd seen on either face.

They were out the door before it even occurred to me to wonder how they knew about Frederich. When it did occur to me, I felt sick to my stomach. That's when I knew I had something to hide.

Two days after their visit, my office phone began to go click when I picked it up.

How I hated doing it, but I went to my friend who was head of our technical work and talked to him. The best way I can describe how I felt about my suspicion of a tap is to say it made me feel guilty and unclean. Don't ask about what. But, don't you know, I had to find out.

I had the most awful time asking my friend—let's call him Sam—about my suspicion, but I finally got it out that I thought my phones were being tapped, both at home and there in the office.

Of course, his first questions were "What did you do?" and "Who's after you?" Considering the state of my nerves, it's a wonder I didn't confess to something. Instead, I screamed at him that I hadn't done anything. I had nothing to hide, so no one should be after me.

But he was no less a child of the American climate of the time than most. He was a decent, honest man and, like his kind, was watching other decent, honest men in our industry go under. Things were a trifle mad.

Bugging wasn't the big industry then that it is now. This was

the pre-007 period. Sam said he had no idea how to find a tap,
but he'd ask friends in the business. Asking that kind of question
in that paranoid time could get one into trouble. It says a lot for
Sam's friendship that he had the courage to do it.

He did find the tap, but he had no idea who was doing the
tapping. He could just read the drain on the line, or whatever he
called it.

It's hard for me to admit, but I thought that if I was being
investigated because of the oboist, I would have to let him go.
It's not to my credit that I called those men at the FBI and told
them that if they wanted, I would not use the man again. They
said that was the last thing they wanted me to do: "Keep him on
the payroll so you can keep an eye on him . . . and don't make
him suspicious." My heart sank. I didn't want to spy on anyone,
and the idea of reporting to them made me feel ill. I couldn't
bring myself to ask them if they were tapping my phone. I was
sure they would say yes, but not tell me why.

# Billy Hicks

I remember that year the way the survivors remember the Titanic. I'm absolutely superstitious about the number nineteen fifty-three. It got so bad I went to an astrologer *and* a numerologist to find out why my perfectly fine life had suddenly become chaotic. I still hate even talking about that time.

Just when the shit hit Carl and Wesley, I was in the middle of trying to raise the cash to buy out Lily's share of the company. We were each half owners, and I was up to my ass in accountants and lawyers trying to see whether going public would solve the problem. It was the only way we could protect Lily's estate.

Lily was dying. Cancer. It was like her that she'd made them tell her how soon or how late she could expect to live, and to press settling a new contract against that deadline. I found it awful and frightening, and, wouldn't you know, it was Lily who was always bucking up my spirits. I didn't know if I could make it alone. I had the business daring, but Lily had the restraint. She'd always let me have my head, but if I started to get in too deep it was always Lily who suggested that a little slowing down and regrouping wouldn't hurt. We were perfect for one another—had been from the very start. She kept us from getting in deeper than would have been wise, when I was all gung-ho to just plunge in.

At the same time I was now supporting my family up in Schenectady. My brothers had gone out on strike, and when the strike was over they'd been laid off. They couldn't find work. Father was dead, so Mother was living with one or another of my brothers. I'd offered to take Mother with me, but she said a very firm no. From what little she knew of my life, she thought I was depraved. But she was proud of her depraved son.

When Teddy was at home, our life was fine. I had no idea

what he was up to at all those AA meetings he went to, but they didn't seem to do him any harm. He was always after me to go to one of those meetings with him, but I never did. I'd gotten rid of my church, I had no intention of trying his. He said it wasn't a church, but he took to praying, so what else would you call it.

But he was wonderful with Lily. I admit that I'm not very good around sick people. I sometimes think I'm afraid of them. But Teddy was always wonderful about that.

Lily was in and out of hospital, and even when she was out, she was constantly going there for some treatment or another. Teddy was always with her, and while she was at home he would move in with her. There were nurses round the clock, but it was Teddy who kept her company and kept her laughing.

I found her poignant, but Teddy didn't, and he wouldn't let me be low around her. "No long faces, and don't you dare ask her how she is," he'd say. "She's rotten sick and you know it, and she knows it, but if she can take it so can you." Teddy could be firm.

Still, it was hard. Lily insisted on going everywhere. She wouldn't stop. We'd get to a party or a theater opening and Teddy would hop out of the car, unfold the wheelchair, and lift her out and get her into it. There wasn't much to Teddy, but by now there was even less to Lily. Does that sound awful? Teddy literally carried Lily through those last months.

I've watched friends go bonkers, and they almost seem to get younger-looking. With Lily, the more she faded, the sharper her mind seemed to get. She would sit in on those meetings about issuing stock in our company, and when the talk got fuzzy, Lily would bring it right back into focus. She'd sit quietly watching and listening with those great feverish eyes just burning, and she didn't miss a thing.

Teddy would always get her ready to go out. He even dressed her. He said the nurses had no sense of style. And the two of them would be in her bedroom laughing and carrying on while he put her makeup on. They seemed to be having the time of their life, but under the circumstances, it just depressed me.

I couldn't imagine life without Lily, but in a way, I'd already lost her, or at least given her up. Teddy didn't.

Of course, in the middle of all that mess, the shit also hit the fan for Carl and Wesley. It is not to my credit to tell you that the evening Teddy lectured me on our need to stand by them, I just sat down and cried. I just couldn't take any more. Christ, but I had a plateful. Lily, family business, and now those two old farts were undermining the government. The whole damned world was coming to an end.

# Robert Regal

I had never liked Lily, and it would be sheer hypocrisy to say that I was deeply concerned over what was happening. I certainly took no pleasure in her condition. Teddy adored her. I was sorry about the situation on his account. He would come to my place and weep for her. Perhaps because I judged my motives as mixed, I was most assiduous in seeing that, as nearly as time allowed, her affairs were organized to the greatest advantage of her personal estate.

In the matter of Carl, when I first heard about his problem, I thought he was imagining things. Carl called me from a public phone booth in Los Angeles. All through the call there was this constant clatter of quarters going into the machine. Carl told me he thought his phone was being tapped, but he had no idea why. Carl was calling to find out if I could move any of his money out of the country and to England. I told him that it could be done, but that he might stand to lose as much as seven percent or more on such a transaction.

Carl lived in Los Angeles, so I didn't pay as much attention to his stories about the FBI and phone taps and investigations and what all as I might have otherwise. I don't mind admitting I was wrong.

Carl was in trouble. As it turned out, so was Wesley. I hadn't paid any attention to any of that McCarthy nonsense. I am, by nature, rather single-minded. It didn't affect any of the stocks in which I dealt, so why bother. However, when it became clear that my client was in trouble, I did my homework. I even bought a television set to follow the news and those un-American Committee hearings.

I was more than a little surprised to see that scoundrel

Seymour among the group surrounding McCarthy. As Wesley would say, there was Seymour center stage. I felt that if Seymour was among that lot, their credentials were dubious.

# Wesley Ober

When I knew it was happening to me I was terrified.

When your friends are being drummed out of a business because they're supposed to be Communists, you commiserate, you even send what you can afford if they hit you up, but, even then, in the back of your mind is the idea that there might be something to the accusations.

If they could shut everybody up, if they could even get Charlie Chaplin, what chance did most poor schmucks stand?

I read everything about the Chaplin affair, because I'd met the great man in the twenties. He surprised me. He was called the Little Tramp, but he was the most cultivated, urbane man imaginable. I was awed by him. And how I loved his movies.

In 1952, his movie *Limelight* opened and was picketed everywhere. I remember one picket's sign very well: It said, KICK THE ALIEN OUT OF THE COUNTRY. Another sign said something about sending him to Russia. How awful. I knew that two of his sons had fought in the war.

I can't remember the details, but in the middle of the fuss over his movie Chaplin had gone abroad, and the government wasn't going to let him back in. I don't know whether they kept him out or he decided not to come back, but he stayed out. He stayed abroad. Once there wasn't a person in this country who didn't love him. Now he was actually hated.

So, when my agent called to say that the Internal Revenue Service was after his files on me, I panicked.

Two men who said they were from the IRS had just shown up at my agent's office with a court order to remove his files on me. My agent wanted to know what I'd done. I told him I hadn't done a damned thing, and then the old darling, who had been raking off ten percent of my salary for almost twenty years, said,

"I hope you have sense enough to be scared." I thanked him for his concern for my mental condition. It must have been right after we spoke that he sat right down to write me he didn't feel he could continue to represent me. That was all right with me. He hadn't gotten me into Sheila's show anyway, and yet he'd taken ten percent of six years' salary.

I knew Carl was in some kind of trouble, and I wondered whether my problem had anything to do with Carl's. I wanted to think it didn't. Throw him to the lions, dear God, but spare my ass. If they'd questioned me about Carl at that time, he would still be in prison.

Now that they'd made me nervous, I became very aware. I began noticing that some days I would have mail—lots of it— and then none for two or three days. Several days' worth of mail would arrive all at once, and I began to notice the way it was sealed. I was sure some of the seals were crimpled, as if they'd been opened and resealed.

I still wish Carl hadn't called, but he called me at the theater—between acts, I might add—to say that he didn't want to scare me, but his phone had been tapped and he suspected that my phone at the hotel was also tapped. Of course I asked *him* what he had done.

Two or three weeks later, Sheila called at ten in the morning. When Sheila was up at ten, you could be sure that the world's days were numbered. Madame said, "Get over here."

When I got there, Madame didn't waste a moment. She asked me what everybody seemed to be asking everybody else: "What have you done?"

I asked, "What do you mean?" and she said, "You tell me." She said that she had been rousted out of bed at eight-thirty by two men who were banging on the door to her suite announcing for everyone on the floor to hear, "FBI!"

It must have been the first time since she was three that she'd let anyone see her without full makeup and costume. Even when we slept together, she either made me leave afterward or she would be up before me and fully made up and dressed when I got up. Stars of her time were never seen as mere mortals.

The FBI men had questioned Sheila for over an hour about me. She said she had been evasive, and that irritated the hell out of me. I told her she needn't have been because I hadn't done anything she need hide from anyone. Evasive, indeed!

She described the men as faintly reptilian and, leave it to her, she said they had on the most awful gray suits and white socks. Sheila hated shabby productions, on or off stage.

I knew Sheila well enough to know that she was shaken. Her voice was pitched too high and she did too much business. She asked me the same questions they'd asked her. Nothing they'd asked told me anything.

Finally Sheila said there was no reason why we should starve to death, so she ordered up breakfast. When we were finished, she said, "They want me to let you go." I was dumbfounded. I couldn't blame her for being afraid. God knows, I was.

I asked her what she intended to do, and she said that she'd been watching a lot of her old friends go under to the anti-Communists and she was deeply grateful that she'd never made a movie that had a brain in its head. She said she was even happy now that she hadn't gotten the second female lead in *Ninotchka*. It was the brainy ones that were in trouble, she said, and she was goddamned if she could figure out what they wanted with the likes of me. I found her comment a mixed consolation.

I finally realized that all the talk was just evasion: Madame had already made a decision and she was going to buckle under. I suppose that's not fair to her. What the FBI wanted it got.

So, I just said, "When do you want me to leave?" I'd never seen her do it, but Sheila actually started to cry. Her face just crumpled up. I wish she hadn't, because I saw her age for the first time. She was in a terrible spot. A nice old gal just trying to make her career carry her for a few more years. I felt sorry for her.

She said, "I just can't buck 'em, honey. I just can't." I said that I knew and tried to console her. Poor old bitch. Poor me.

The upshot was that she would keep me on the payroll and advance me money to get me to New York, and she would pay her lawyer to help me. In that time, helping an old pal took guts. Unfortunately neither of us had any idea how the lawyer would help me clear myself of a crime I couldn't even remember.

Well, it had been six good years with her. She'd bailed me out of Hollywood and let me have six very good years. I didn't think that at the time.

I needed help, but I didn't know what kind. I knew Robert had some sense, so I packed up and booked on the Twentieth Century to New York.

I felt like a fool doing it, but I wrote a letter to Carl and found a mutual friend who would hand-deliver it to him on the Coast. By now I didn't trust my phone or the mails. And then I started asking myself the most popular question of the time: What did I do?

All I could think of was that dreadful pro-Russian movie I'd worked in for one day near the end of the war. If the FBI was after people for making rotten movies, I had my own blacklist.

# Carl Mason

I was in a recording session when Wesley's friend showed up with the letter. I had to interrupt the session, because the man said he couldn't wait and Wesley told him not to give his letter to anyone but me. I had to give the musicians a break—and that cost a lot of money, I can tell you—and go see the man.

The man told me Wesley was leaving that show he'd been touring in forever and was going back to New York. Wesley had told him that it was of the "greatest importance" that I receive the letter in person. I thought, it's more of Wesley's melodrama and it's hardly reason for costing me a lot of money. I thanked the man with as little bad grace as I could manage and went back to work. I loved Wesley, but I thought, "Leave it to him to turn something as simple as sending a letter into a Hitchcock movie." I wish you could have seen Wesley work. He could turn a simple cross from left stage to right into a whole new scene. Everything but curtsies and cartwheels.

I just stuffed the letter in my pocket and went back to work.

I almost forgot the letter until after dinner, and then I went and fetched it and read it. I owed Wesley an apology.

It was the worst news I ever got, or damned near. Wesley told me what had happened and what he suspected. Jesus, it *was* a Hitchcock movie.

After years, I was finally planning a vacation. I'd applied for a passport months earlier, and then forgotten about it. Now that Frederich and I were about a month from leaving, I had my secretary follow it up. She was told that there was some problem with my passport application and that I shouldn't depend on having it in the near future. No, she was told, there was nothing I could do to straighten things out.

What happened to Frederich just made me more depressed than ever. Frederich had been called before the immigration authorities and questioned at length about his association with me. They had taken him to a room in the cellar of the building and a Mr. O'Conner had interviewed Frederich for two hours about his life since he came to the United States. Frederich said that every question he'd been asked had something to do with either our gay friends or his relationship with me. Frederich said that the entire interview was taken down by a stenotypist who sat in a far corner just tapping away at his machine and never once looking up.

We were very frightened. Remember, Frederich was an alien with no rights. They could have him out of the country in hours.

That O'Conner man asked him directly about the homosexual activities of his friends, and intimated that if he would report on a few friends he would make life easier for himself. Frederich was a child of Nazi Germany, he knew better. Frederich said he knew how the Nazis interrogated, and he said O'Conner was an amateur—but learning fast. I found it odd when Frederich said it, but he seemed as disturbed by O'Conner's obviously prurient interest as by the questions.

O'Conner would say, "We know that your friend So-and-so frequents a bar in Beverly Hills known to be a homosexual gathering place. What do you know about the man, the place, the people there? Have you been to that place? What do you mean you don't remember? Are you trying to hinder our investigation?"

Investigation of what?

When O'Conner finished with him, he told Frederich that he would be sent a transcript of the interview and would be called to reply to it. In the meantime they were going to examine his immigrant status to determine his "desirability."

Frederich came home that night shaken, but, to his everlasting credit, he was more angry than shaken. He asked me if he had left one totalitarian state to come to another. By the time they let him go, he hadn't incriminated one of our friends. "Let them suspect all they want," he said. "If I don't tell them, they'll have to find someone else to betray their friends, but not me." It took courage for him to do that. All the while he was telling me what happened, I just looked at him and thought, I'm going to lose you.

We'd been living with that for a week when Wesley's letter arrived. That was the week that really finished matters for us.

Everyone who worked in the movie business went to bed early. Most of us had six or seven A.M. calls, so one didn't stay up late. You were ready for bed at ten and damned tired by then.

I can still tell you the exact time it happened: two A.M. right on the button, because I came wide awake from a deep sleep. The pounding and yelling would have wakened the dead.

Someone was banging furiously on our front door screaming, "Open up, we know all about you!" Over and over, "Open up, we know all about you!" To this day, I can't tell you what went on in my mind, but I had the sense not to turn on any lights—to stay away from the door and call the police. I don't think it took them two minutes to get there. I heard their siren and then I saw flashlights bobbing across the lawn and the police yelled, "Hold it, right there!" Then there was a scuffling at the door, and the banging and yelling suddenly stopped.

I was scared to death, but I made myself go near the window in the living room and look out at the door. The police were just talking to the man at our door. They looked quite cozy. The man fished out a billfold and held something toward the police, and then I actually heard them laugh. That was almost scarier than the shouting. Finally, all three just walked away, chatting like old chums.

When I had courage enough to turn on the lights, Frederich made coffee and we stayed up.

I knew it was probably pointless, but I called the police. I asked them what the patrolmen had reported. The policeman who answered said it was just a drunk. I said that I wanted to know what I should do to press charges, and the policeman said, "You want to make more trouble for yourself?"

By then, I would have taken any action I could, hired the best lawyers. But how do you take action against what you can't see, against undefined accusations? I didn't know. I still don't.

Looking back on that awful night, what was done seems such a pointless and childish kind of intimidation. But it did its job: it terrified me. It also made me come to my senses. "They" were after me. "They" were after Frederich and me, and I had the feeling they meant to destroy me.

I think that if one doesn't hate, it's hard to imagine that other people do. They can hate murderously, and when it can be justified and sanctioned as a good cause, one can just sink without a trace in the general chaos. I saw it all the time out there in Hollywood.

Well, I wasn't without money or resources. I was damned if I would go under like a lot of my friends. I'd get out, before I'd go under.

The next day I started arranging to delegate all my responsibilities at the company for the time being. That wasn't too hard, since I'd blocked out almost two months for vacation. I called Robert in New York and told him that Frederich and I were coming there. I told him something of what had been going on. I left the details for later. Robert was going to book us into the St. Regis. He said that Wesley was there already and went everywhere in a large coat, a floppy hat, and sunglasses.

# Billy Hicks

Oh, a lot of my friends from the old Washington days just flew out of that town, mostly State Department types with a sprinkling of Voice of America people. My dear, if you were with the State Department in those days, everybody just supposed you were gay.

I certainly knew the purge was on down there, because I got dozens of contracts to decorate New York apartments for fleeing State Department "undesirables." As a friend said, the State Department may be a hotbed of homosexuals, but that mattress is full of money.

When Wesley and Carl fled back to New York, I couldn't for the life of me figure out what in God's name they'd done to get the FBI after them. I invited them both to stay with me, but they said it was as well if we weren't that closely associated, until they knew why they were being investigated.

I was insanely busy at that time, so most of what I heard about things came from Teddy, and that wasn't much.

Teddy was constantly after me to stand by them. He made it all something of a cause. I finally got exasperated with Teddy and told him to tell me how I could help or to shut up about all that sticking together. Well, Teddy told me that I might use some of my contacts in Washington to see if I could find out why they were after Carl and Wesley. Asking that kind of question was like poking a hornet's nest. Not only did no one know anything, they didn't want to know anything. And what could I ask? Excuse me, but the FBI is after two friends of mine. Could you find out if they're wanted because they're Commies or fags? Oh, I see, they're wanted for being both. It was a question I didn't want to ask and didn't think should be asked.

It's so long ago that I suppose it can't hurt anyone to talk about it now, but I did do a fair amount of sleeping around when I was in Washington. I never talked about it. I was discreet. But I was also in my twenties and Teddy couldn't be with me. Well, that's a long time ago. My point is that I slept with some rather important people. Most I could remember, but what would I ask them? Nobody had the guts to buck McCarthy. He might have been a crazy old drunk, but so was Nero. Even Eisenhower wouldn't interfere, even when McCarthy went after the Army.

I finally did make two calls, but couldn't find out a thing. What difference would knowing have made? As it turned out, it wouldn't have changed a thing.

# Robert Regal

If it hadn't been for Teddy I never would have touched the matter. There they were running about like the proverbial chickens. I kept pointing out to them that they could not take action until they knew what was going on. To be sure, Carl and Wesley had their hotel phones tapped, but that didn't tell them anything. In my field, they were in what is called the futures market, and I always advise my clients to stay out of that kind of business.

I told Teddy the best he could do was to try and keep them calm. Undoubtedly, it was that Hollywood background. It seems to incline those people toward drama. I did finally agree to help them for Teddy's sake . . . only if they would cooperate fully, with no play-acting.

I began by arranging a clandestine meeting. Lest you think I'm given to melodrama, let me explain my thinking. My being of help might well depend on the FBI's not knowing I was involved. As we all knew in that era, anyone who helped the suspect was himself suspect, even lawyers. Almost all lawyers were loath to take on a tainted client. Those helping the accused were more often than not added to the list of suspects. Hence, the clandestine meeting, foolish as that may sound.

Wesley, of course, turned it into something of a social occasion. He brought glasses and liquor and ice, and insisted we toast to our first reunion in ten years. I pointed out that an assembly of fugitives hardly constituted a reunion. I also pointed out that I would prefer their sober attention.

I proposed that I hire a research assistant for each of them to help each compile a detailed record of dates and events over the past twenty years. I explained that the FBI was acting on some personal information and that, no matter how remote the event, it might be the cause of their interest. Also, I hoped that we might find an event or person common to Carl and Wesley. I also suggested that the research people buy or get copies of every blacklist currently circulating in New York and Hollywood. Wesley and Carl had either done something or someone had thrown them rather casually into the investigation, a not uncommon action. My two old associates needed to know as much about themselves as the FBI knew. I proposed going over every name in every film either had worked on and cross-checking against blacklists. I would personally review their income-tax statements as far back as they went. Tax records are extraordinarily revelatory journals.

Carl's life was relatively circumspect, so assembling data on him and his associates would be comparatively simple. Comparatively, I say. Wesley was another matter. The man was rather wide-ranging in his activities. I hesitate to say indiscriminate and indiscreet, but I don't think Wesley would argue with that. Be rather pleased with himself, if I know Wesley.

I estimated that it would cost about three thousand dollars each to do what I proposed. Of course I had to advance Wesley the money.

I hired two very discreet people who did client investigations for me. I never take on clients without vetting them. I don't use sources like Dun & Bradstreet. Not nearly thorough enough for my purposes.

Things quieted down for the two "fugitives," as they termed themselves. It's as well, because it took my people almost two months to compile their dossiers. In the meantime I started moving substantial amounts of Carl's money to England and hired a firm to look into making Carl's company public. That way, he could derive income as the principal stockholder without being active in the company. I should have used a man to assemble the data on Wesley. The poor woman who did the job couldn't even look me in the eye when she delivered the material on him.

The researchers didn't find much, but it was enough in those days. Carl's friend Jimmy had performed in a concert for an anti-Franco group in Los Angeles and Carl had sent the group a twenty-five-dollar donation. Carl had worked on seven films on which people accused of Communist activities had been employed. Carl had done some work on *Mission to Moscow* and had been part of a team that advised Mosfilm and on Russian soil. Wesley had done all sorts of things, most of which I won't go into. On his debit side was that awful movie about Russian peasants that Teddy had dragged me to, and a lot of friends who were suspect. Since Wesley seemed to know everyone, that was bound to happen. Also, while Wesley was doing that theater work in the Army, he had arranged for the Russian Army Chorus, which was here on a goodwill tour, to appear at some Army bases. To be sure, not much, but enough. We also found that both their names were on several blacklists. But how or why, I couldn't discover.

I still have those dossiers. I'm not a pack rat, but I have an instinct for what is worth saving. As it developed, that instinct resulted in the most distasteful encounter of my career.

# Wesley Ober

The FBI didn't appreciate my sense of humor. When they came busting into my hotel room that night at three A.M., I told them I thought they kept very peculiar hours.

The gentlemen in gray had come to tell me that I was being summoned down to their headquarters that day for a preliminary inquiry into my alleged pro-Communist activities. I must say, *that* left me without an exit line.

I got dressed and went down to the lobby and called the clan. I'd been doing that since my phone started going click. I reached Carl just as his invitation was being delivered in person by two men. I'll give those Yahoos one thing, they knew how to put the fear of God into a fellow.

When I called Billy, Teddy answered, and I told him that Carl and I were both being hailed down to FBI headquarters that morning. I was sorry I told Teddy and not Billy. Teddy cared so much about all of us, and the poor baby was scared to death for us. Billy told me that Teddy cried all that night.

Carl and I were due for our interview at eight-thirty that morning. Carl called me at seven-thirty, from his bugged phone to my bugged phone. He said, "Now they'll have two recordings of the same conversation. I hope they don't mix them up." I thought that was pretty sassy of him.

Carl said he didn't think we would be interviewed together, and neither of us knew how long it would take, but we agreed that whoever got out first would wait for the other in the lobby . . . assuming either of us ever saw the light of day again.

Well, I had never played a spy before, so I had no idea how to dress for the occasion. I thought of wearing a gray suit and white socks, and confusing the hell out of them, but I settled on a very sincere blue suit. I have never dressed as carefully for a role. I

233

used a great deal of deodorant that morning. I remember thinking it was the only protection I had.

I didn't see Carl in the lobby of their office building when I got there, so I went on up to the floor I'd been told to report to. I went up in the elevator feeling like Ronald Colman playing Sydney Carton.

A receptionist with matching beady eyes took my name and asked me to be seated until an escort arrived to take me into what she called the "secure area." As I was being "escorted" to the room, I said to her, "I hope I see you again," with more irony than I'd intended. My God, they were a frosty lot. I was sure that if I'd hit any of them, clockwork would have fallen out.

They put me in an interior room with no windows, nothing on the walls, and just a table with three chairs. There was a grill over the ceiling fixture to keep desperate felons like me from stealing their light bulbs.

I sat alone in that room for over half an hour, which gave me entirely too much time to think about my sins. I had no idea what I would be asked, but I was determined to take my time answering and I gave myself a lecture on not trying to be funny. As an audience, they were like playing Dubuque on Good Friday.

Finally, a young man came in. He opened the door and just stared at me for the longest time with the most disapproving look on his mug. Then he came within arm's length and handed me a sheet of paper. He said, "We won't need you just now. You'll report to that address in two days. Now, wait here. You'll be taken out." Then he just left.

I sat down and looked at the sheet of paper. There was no letterhead, just an address in Washington, the date and time.

I was shown out and to the elevators. For some reason, I was more frightened by this nameless address than I had been by the FBI. Now there was not only no accusations, but whoever was after us was completely nameless.

I wasn't surprised to see Carl in the lobby when I got there. He held up his matching sheet of paper and said, "Now what?" I shook my head.

It was only a little after nine, and hordes of people were pouring into the office building. It was awful, but I just stood there crying like a damned fool. Carl said, "I know," and he put his arm around me and got me out of there.

# Carl Mason

It was the ghastliest outing I've ever been on. The six of us had taken adjoining compartments on the Washington train. There was too much gloom: We couldn't have stood being cramped in just one. We couldn't be too close.

Wesley insisted on putting a good face on things, though I couldn't imagine why. He had his hotel pack a large picnic basket for us so we wouldn't have to go to the dining car, and he was being so jolly that we all took to yelling at him. I told him that he was like a jester in a tumbrel. He was quiet for all of five minutes.

Teddy was still, except that his eyes kept tearing up and his nose ran constantly. Wesley told theater stories to the air, because no one was paying him the least attention. I sat worrying about the future, and Robert sat with the table pulled down, sorting through heaps of paper. Frederich was asleep in the next compartment. Billy was in there, too. He was along for moral support, though that never was his forte. But Lily and Teddy had both put the screws on him to come along.

Robert had enough files with him to run IBM. When Wesley asked him what all that stuff was, he just got huffy and said that he wasn't in the habit of hauling around "stuff." Billy kept telling Teddy to stop sniveling. I kept telling Wesley to shut up. Robert kept going *Sssh!* to all of us. You can see what kind of mood we were in.

We had no idea what the summons meant or whom we were to see or what was to happen to Wesley and me. I'd asked Robert about taking a lawyer, and he told me he felt it would be a waste, since no summons had been issued and we could not be placed before a grand jury or even the House Committee without some warning. He said that our date to appear in Washington was likely preliminary. He was lying.

So I just sat on the train and worried. I worried about getting enough money out of the country to take care of Frederich if he was forced to run. He'd be alone, and we weren't sure where he'd be safe. I still didn't have my passport.

# Billy Hicks

We were up all night after those FBI folks busted in on Wesley and Carl. I was worried, but Teddy was absolutely hysterical. Well, he always was a little high-strung. He got furious with me because he thought I didn't take the whole mess as seriously as he took it. I told him I did take it seriously, but since there was nothing I could do to help, there was no sense in both of us getting hysterical.

Of course Teddy had to get on the phone to Robert and get him all stirred up. And I didn't like it one bit when Teddy ran off to Robert's that night. Teddy kept insisting that Robert could help, and I told him that nobody could help. Robert had already done all he could.

If Eisenhower couldn't do anything about McCarthy, how in hell was I going to, or Robert, or anyone except God, and even He seemed singularly unconcerned.

I was able to be of some help on the trip. Washington was jammed, but I managed to get all of us into the Hay-Adams for two nights.

That night in Washington was as gloomy as the train ride, and we dined in our rooms out of sight, like fugitives. Wesley and Carl's appointment was for very early the next morning, eight or so. So we all turned in. Being close to one another was very abrasive.

# Robert Regal

I suppose I'm still being accused of perpetuating the awful suspense for those two. I leave such dramatics to people like Melvin Belli. I had to get dangerously ahead of myself to even spare Wesley and Carl those FBI interviews, but after Teddy came over that night and told me how Carl and Wesley had been invaded and the FBI's Gestapo tactics, I'm afraid my temper let me do it.

I still feel it was reckless doing what I did. I still didn't feel assured I could marshal a case. I knew that I might well make things worse instead of better. I explained all that to Teddy. I told him, "Don't get their hopes up."

If I'd said a word to anyone, they might well have gone off half-cocked.

Before I did anything I had to make sure that neither Wesley nor Carl were involved in any Communist activities. I knew them both well, but I've known clients well who have given even me bad turns with surprises such as illegitimate children, blackmailing mistresses, and, in one case, two living wives. Oh, no, I don't go by what people tell me; I go by what I personally discover to be true.

Once I felt assured that they were indeed victims of a pointless vendetta, I felt morally obliged to help.

I had the devil's own time reaching Seymour at seven A.M. that morning. It took Teddy calling Lily, who called a very prominent scoundrel, to get Seymour's private number. I called him, reintroduced myself as a former OPA associate, and said that I was in possession of all the relevant files on his stamp-production work for OPA. I suggested that he might feel more secure if he had the material for his personal files. Seymour was a man who got right to the point, and he said, "Who do you want killed?" Vivid man.

I said that I had two clients who were either subjects of his or the FBI's interest. I could verify their patriotism, since I had extensive dossiers on both that validated their rectitude. I told Seymour about the scheduled FBI interviews and suggested he might be able to spare everyone wasted effort. I said that looking into their lives was a waste of government money, because they were innocent. Seymour said, "No one is innocent."

I told Seymour that I would be happy to present my clients, their credentials, and his OPA files at his convenience, and see what kind of rapprochement might be worked out.

The effectiveness of my files depended on the relationship of McCarthy to that man Seymour. As I said, I had started following McCarthy's activities and, often as not, Seymour would be nearby, either in a story or a picture, and, usually, on the television. What I couldn't determine was his relationship to McCarthy or his status. Seymour was an *éminence grise*.

I had to discover whether Seymour was valuable enough to McCarthy to make McCarthy want to hold on to him or to fear being embarrassed by him. I had, also, to reassure myself that my files on Seymour's chicanery at the OPA constituted sufficient proof to pose a real threat. Legally, the statute of limitations left the files impotent. Their value lay wholly in their worth as damaging publicity.

As soon as I hung up on Seymour I raced to my office with Teddy and he helped me remove the OPA files to a private office I kept to protect the most personal data on my clients. It was a wise move. My offices were broken into that night. When it came, Watergate held no surprises for me.

I was still at work reviewing and organizing those files all the way down to Washington and half the night after we got there.

I hesitate to use the phrase, but I've often heard business associates say that one should never get into a pissing contest with a skunk.

I didn't like that Seymour fellow and I had no intention of going into any contest with him whatsoever. If I was to face him down, I would have to do so armed with well-organized evidence, clear goals, and even with exits prepared. Seymour was not a man to be trusted, so his word alone would not suffice in any argument. Each step must be taken with some delicacy, and I would have to be sure, before a foot was set down, that the ground ahead was firm.

# Wesley Ober

It was just like a Perry Mason episode.

Robert doesn't even like to talk about it, and when he does it sounds like he's reading the label on a can. But there was drama that morning. I've always thought I might write it up.

*Scene:* A Washington mansion owned by an anonymous millionaire with a taste for Victorian Gothic, inside and out. In a vast library with floor-to-ceiling books, the principals are discovered seated, studies in brown, awaiting the entrance of the man who holds their fate in his hands. I used the tense atmosphere I felt when I was reduced to doing a package of *The Night of January Sixteenth* on the summer circuit. It was a cheap production. The real-life production I was in that morning was handsomely mounted. Well, if I was going under, I was doing it in style.

Robert had called Carl and me at six-thirty that morning, and he told us to meet him in the dining room at seven. He said he "considered it a meeting of some consequence." I knew Robert well enough to know that meant "important."

When Carl and I got down, Robert was in the dining room with Teddy. After we'd ordered, Robert told us he was making no promises, but that he might have the leverage to get Carl and me out of the mess. After a lot of heavy-duty prologue, he said that he thought some old files showed that one of McCarthy's right-hand men was a crook. That was Seymour. He said that if it was okay with us he would go along and do the talking, and I told him that I would break the rule of a lifetime and shut up. Carl looked so low I think he would have agreed to anything. He was worrying for two. Robert was his usual miserly self with details.

He said that Teddy would stay at the hotel and guard the files, because Robert had reason to distrust this Seymour fellow.

So we got to this baronial place in Georgetown at eight-thirty on the button. Robert squared his homburg and strode right up to the door and rang the bell. Then there was this long wait and, my God, a butler answered. Robert barely glanced at the man, said, "We're expected," and barged right in. The butler showed us into the library, and I swear he actually backed out when he left us.

Robert was the only person who seemed lively enough to even bother looking the room over. He was up and down the library ladder like a monkey. He was unnerving. He made me hold onto his briefcase, and I sat pinned in my chair by that damned heavy thing. Carl just sat near the window looking out on a garden.

I'd seen Seymour's picture often enough, but I wasn't prepared for the man himself. When this Seymour entered the room, I literally wanted to run. He was smallish and dark, and no more than thirty or so, but there was something very old about him and something very dead. I've spent a long time looking for the right word for him, and the best I could ever do was "Satanic." As he walked through the door he said, "Which one is Regal?" Robert said, "I'm he," and came over and took his briefcase from me.

Seymour just stood with his back to the door and said, "Just spell out what you're up to and let's get this over."

Robert wasn't going to be hurried. He went and sat down and opened his briefcase and took out a folder. Then he read down a list of what had been happening to Carl and me, reading one and two and three. *One,* Mr. Ober was first aware of his phone being tapped on such-and-such a date. *Two,* Mr. Mason had knowledge of this and that. Seymour hadn't moved from the door, but he was starting to fidget. Robert got to about number ten when Seymour told him to cut the shit, which didn't go down at all well with Robert. Robert made a face like Edna Mae Oliver, and said that he would be more than happy not to prolong the matter, but if all the items on his agenda were to be resolved, an orderly process would eventually expedite matters. Dry as dust, he was. He finished reading the list.

Seymour stayed where he was. Robert was getting on his nerves. Robert was using an old stage trick to create suspense, wearing the audience's nerves thin.

Then Robert stopped what he was doing and said, ever so casually, that since it was early and he estimated the meeting would take about an hour, he should like coffee brought. Seymour looked apoplectic, but I guess he was so surprised that he rang for the butler and ordered coffee.

Robert said "Thank you," and then started to list what he called something like "requests for assistance in the following." Listening to the legalese was almost like hearing a foreign language, but it was all clear enough if you paid attention. Robert told Seymour that he wanted Carl and me off every blacklist that was circulating. He wanted the FBI and the tax people called off, and he wanted our files destroyed by the FBI and by Seymour's committee. Robert said he wanted the immigration authorities called off Frederich's case, and that he would appreciate Carl's passport within the week. Just like that—tick, tick, tick.

When Robert was finished, Seymour just looked at him for the longest time. He was sizing Robert up and looking to see if it was bluff. Finally Seymour said, "That'll cost," and Robert said he had two years' worth of OPA files, which should cover matters.

Seymour said he had Carl and me "by the balls" and he wasn't sure that old scandal was enough to make it worthwhile. It was very slangy of Robert, but he actually said, "Let's call a spade a spade." I can take him off pretty well:

"It is not only the files, not just the peculation in stamps, there is your alliance to that rather indelicate matter of providing companionable young gentlemen for a fee. Hearsay, to be sure, but you surely know the publicity value of hearsay, these days, especially the most scandalous and invidious. Consider what price your committee would put on what I know—consider the value to the press of intimate news from inside your committee."

Barrymore couldn't have delivered the lines better. And don't you love the phrase "companionable young gentlemen"? I've never forgotten it. I quite forgot my ass was swaying in a sling and just sat there enjoying the hell out of myself.

When Robert finished saying all that, Seymour fixed him with a look that was pure evil, and he had the eyes for it. Dead eyes, but still hungry.

The coffee arrived and Seymour didn't move toward it, so Robert got up and poured cups for Carl and me and then asked

Seymour in the politest tones if he would care for a cup. I thought it was the loveliest bit of business to show who was in control.

Seymour was a million miles away, with *Scheming!* written all over that surly face.

When Seymour did come back, he came back strong. He said the files were beyond the statute of limitations. "Embarrassing," Seymour said, "but explainable and not that damaging so long after the war." He thought they could be explained or just buried. Then he told Robert that if Robert brought up that other matter, they'd both be in the shithouse and they'd probably both go under.

Robert just gazed ever so calmly at Seymour and said, "I know." He said that he knew the files were not much to pay for keeping us out of harm's way. He said he hoped they would be, because, as much as he hated going into the mud with Seymour, he would do it. He said something like, "Everything in me is repelled by dealing with you, but lines must be drawn."

Robert said that he felt that he was behaving as dishonorably as many others by coming this close to blackmail. He told Seymour that he wasn't sure who was after us or why, but he guessed that Seymour's position and power could solve our problems . . . whatever they were—and we never did find out.

I knew Robert didn't want to be involved, but there he was.

Robert said he'd typed up the list of things he wanted Seymour's "assistance" on. He said he'd leave it if Seymour cared to give it some thought. Seymour said that he wasn't deaf and he could remember. The man was edgy. Then Seymour asked where the files were, and Robert said that he could have them in Seymour's hands an hour after Seymour delivered a letter signed by McCarthy himself saying that the Committee's rigorous (Robert's word) investigation had shown that Carl and I were good Americans.

Then Seymour started doing the most startling thing. He began playing with himself, as unselfconsciously as an ape. It should have been funny. We all looked somewhere else. It was repulsive. Then Seymour said, "Cocksuckers. You're degenerate cocksuckers, and I want you out of my sight." Then he said he'd have the letter handed over as soon as he'd given the files a once-over. Robert said that was agreeable.

Then Seymour asked about copies of the files, and Robert said, "Not copies, but a copy." There was *a* copy. He said that

Seymour would have to take the word of a gentleman that he would safely retain it only to preclude any second thoughts Seymour might have. Robert said he had never reneged on an agreement.

Robert said all that with such complete dignity that Seymour looked confused. But why should he trust Robert? On the other hand, there wasn't much choice, and when he looked at Carl and me, I got the feeling he thought we weren't worth all this trouble. No matter what Seymour thought, I think he knew that Robert meant what he said and that if Seymour fucked around with him, Robert would be the first into the shithouse, followed by as many reporters as he could round up. I could see Robert on the tube talking about "companionable young gentlemen" and confusing the hell out of the reporters.

Well, we got our letter and our sullied souls were turned from slush to driven snow and our phones stopped going click.

God knows what would have happened to us if it hadn't been for Robert. Have I made him sound like a hero? I hope so, and I'd love to see his face when he reads this. I tease him about the way he talks, but I was very happy for that precise, uninflected voice that day. It carried more weight than Olivier.

Do you know *Henry V*?

> We few, we happy few, we band of brothers;
> For he to-day that sheds his blood with me
> Shall be my brother; be he ne'er so vile,
> This day shall gentle his condition.

If it hadn't been for Robert, Carl and Frederich might have been "eating the bitter bread of banishment" and I might have been working as somebody's gardener. We were saved by "a little *Robert* in the night."

When we left the house, I started to thank Robert, and he turned to Carl and me and told us we owed him about two hundred dollars each for the cost of photostating the files.

There was a lovely party in Billy's suite that evening. Teddy gave Robert a long, loving hug that pleased the hell out of Robert, and actually made him blush. Billy just stood looking at them and frowned. Then Robert looked murderous while we sang "For He's a Jolly Good Fellow" and Carl offered a toast to him. The champagne was prewar Mumm's *blanc de blanc*. It gave me one of the most expensive hangovers I've ever had.

It was very unnerving last year when I was walking down Second Avenue and this small man hopped out of a Rolls right in front of me. I almost bumped into him. I looked down and it was Seymour, naturally a much older Seymour. He recognized me. It was awful to see that evil face again. There was I hauling my A & P shopping bag home, while Tootsie was being limoed around town. I told the story to Robert and said something high-minded about the injustice of it all, and Robert just looked at me as if I'd peed in my pants.

# Carl Mason

It took some smart-ass kid to get me moving after that Seymour flap. The "kid" had written a piece for the *Times* saying that movie music as we had known it would soon be a thing of the past. He went on to talk about the jazz scores that were having a vogue just then and about one movie that had no music at all. He consigned Tiomkin and Newman and Korngold and the likes of me to what he called the "senescent school of manipulative musical mush." We were not only passe, we were the victims of alliterative overkill.

How I fumed over that article. How I loved having something other than that awful Communist mess to think about. I gave that article a lot of attention. It was just the old business of the Young Turk wagging his finger at the Old Fart, and telling him to get out of the way.

My life had never turned on large events. The best things that have happened to me always seem to be accidents. That article gave me the anger I needed to finally chuck it all in. Such a little thing by such a little critic, but it did the trick. Someone said my music wasn't wanted. Hollywood was intolerable and I was *de trop,* and I said, "The hell with the whole thing."

Robert helped me reorganize my business, and it went public; we issued stock. Robert's fee was not inconsiderable and worth every cent. Frederich and I packed it in and went to London. We bought a lovely flat with all "mod cons" and spent a year just touring around Europe. We went everywhere but Germany. Frederich couldn't face going back. Besides, he had nothing to go back to. We were happy.

# Billy Hicks

Lily's funeral was everything a doyenne of the interior-design world could have wanted. I'm sure the *Times* was hard put as to whether to put it on the social pages or with obituaries. Acres of black wool crêpe dresses and pearls on the ladies and paper yarmulkes on the men.

I didn't want to go. I wanted to hole up somewhere and hide. Teddy literally dragged me into the limousine. I told him that I would make a perfect fool of myself, and I did as I'd promised.

When my parents died I went up to Schenectady and took care of arrangements. It was a sad time, but they were old and I knew that someday I would lose them. I wasn't unmoved or indifferent to losing them, but I could accept their going as a natural part of things. I suppose the difference is that I "lost" my parents, but Lily died on me. It's odd to be angry at someone for dying on you, but I was in a rage at Lily. My parents didn't leave me *alone*, Lily did. Losing Lily made me an orphan.

Lily left a very large trust for Teddy, which surprised everybody but Robert, who I'm sure had a hand in that. I thought it was one of her dimmer ideas, but trust Lily. Teddy started doing good works. He endowed an alcoholism ward at a hospital in Lily's name, which caused a great deal of conjecture about Lily's private drinking habits. Teddy was involved in every aspect of setting it up. Frankly, I thought he'd drink himself to death with the money, but he found something he was remarkably good at, though, God knows, you wouldn't get me to deal with that scrungy lot they brought into that place. I never saw them, but Teddy would describe some of them, often over dinner, till I took to getting up and leaving the table every time he started.

Then he started dunning our friends for contributions to the ward. I thought the whole thing in dreadful taste, but it gave Teddy something he could call his own.

Lily left half of her half of the business to me. I didn't need it, except to retain the majority of stock.

I commissioned a chic portraitist to paint Lily for our boardroom. Lily would have had a good laugh over that. He painted her very *grande dame*. The woman in that painting would never have told someone to fuck off. The woman in the painting would never have been as shrewdly kind as Lily could be. The painter dressed Lily in velvet. I kept the thing around because it always made me smile to think what Lily would have said about it.

I suppose it was very sentimental of me, but I commissioned a bulb farm to develop a new lily and name it after her. The Gusmin lily. I still see those lilies every so often in classy florists, and every year the grower sends me a dozen bulbs. The lilies are a very pale pink with streaks of green, and they're very sturdy.

# Robert Regal

To say the least, I was very surprised when the mayor's office called me and asked me to be on his fiscal advisory committee. I admit I was flattered, but I didn't know where I would find the time. I had several business friends on the committee, so it was very hard to say no. Eventually I didn't.

As can happen with that kind of involvement, one thing led to another . . . hospital boards, political fund-raising, two corporate boards of directors. All of which brought even more business to my consulting firm.

I worked with Teddy one or two nights a week on setting up and running the Gusmin Memorial Alcoholism Ward.

It was a most satisfying life.

I've avoided your question, because I don't think there's a satisfactory answer. Well, let's be done with it.

I envy men whose bodies make no demands on them. I know a lot of such men. Their work becomes enough. But there was never enough work for me, despite all I undertook. The demands my body makes on me make me angry. I wonder where is my willpower, my resolve, but such demands are beyond logic: They may even make one act against one's own best interests. I've seen a lot of that in my time. Friends ruined by affairs that land them in the courts. It's sad and foolish. I was not much better. I restrained what I still consider the darker side of my nature. I know. It's a funny, old-fashioned phrase, but nothing more apt occurs to me.

Each time willpower failed, I'd capitulate and call a most discreet service I'd heard of in a roundabout way. The wife of a client came to me to discuss her husband. He was an altogether good husband and father, but she found out about his occasional liaisons with young men in hotels. She also found out who provided the young men and asked me, as a friend, whether she should act against the people she thought responsible for her husband's downfall. I suggested that she might well make a bad situation worse, as well as involving many others.

I kept the information on the service for a year before I called them. I half hoped that they had gone out of business, but they answered. I hung up. Of course, I finally became a client.

I've never told anyone. My compeers have all offered to "fix me up," as they call it—Teddy, Carl, Wesley, Billy, the lot of them. I couldn't stand their knowing. No matter what they may have felt about me, they could never do any less than respect me. Yet, every time I used that service I gave away a bit of my self-respect.

I've sometimes wished I'd been a drunk like Teddy. Society has the means for dealing with that problem, it can look the other way and feel pity, even approval. The Irish call it a good man's failing. Society offers us no such compassion, it won't even let us be.

What is it the Catholics say? "Confession is good for the soul." It was never a sin. I just failed myself. Odd that in all areas of my work, I've never been less than totally reliable. I doubted everything about myself every time I opened my door to one of those young men.

# Wesley Ober

I gave a going-away party for Carl and Frederich at the Faisan d'Or, a restaurant over on Sixth Avenue, because that was the only place Robert would go with a lot of men. It was mostly gay, but gray-flannel gay, and there was always a scattering of women, who were always seated just inside the front window to confuse passersby. I would have preferred Celeste, but it was a party we just couldn't have without Robert.

I could have afforded something a lot better. I'd had luck again. I'd been signed to six months on a new dramatic series on radio. It was called *Romance,* and I was to be one of the regular leads. Not what I would have chosen, but there was still decent money in radio. The show only took one day a week, and that would give me time to look around for stage work.

It was the worst party I ever gave. Carl looked dead tired and Freddy just couldn't cheer him up, so he stopped trying and just slumped down. They were going to London, and forever, as far as any of us knew. Billy and Teddy were low, because Lily was back in the hospital and there really wasn't anything more the doctors could do for her. Robert was uncomfortable about being in public with so many men, and he kept looking around as if he expected the vice squad to rush in shooting. I kept thinking that this might be the last time we'd all be together for a long time—maybe never again. That idea didn't do much to cheer *me* up, and I was sorry I'd even thought of it.

We were all a little punch-drunk from all that had been going on. Anyone who looked at us would have thought it was a wake, but they wouldn't have known which one of us to bury first.

I sat there trying to write a good curtain line, trying to create a mood like something in *Three Comrades.* Movies always got

255

through the bad patches with style. Reality is very uncoopera-
tive. We all just sank to the occasion.

We didn't actually get down to being sullen and surly with one
another, but we were certainly snappish.

We were all relieved when the whole damned dinner was over.
We all went out and I hailed them cabs and they all fled in
different directions. I was relieved to see them go.

All through dinner I'd had my eye on a young gentleman at
the bar, so I went back into the restaurant and cheered myself
up.

My God, that lot could be difficult.

# PART 9

---

# "When I'm Sixty-Four"*
## Two Decades
## 1960–1979

*Beatles song of the era which questions the durability of affection.

The sixties made extraordinary promises and then poisoned them. We went from the first black sit-ins through race riots to the assassination of Martin Luther King, Jr. We voted for the hope of John Kennedy and lost a measure of innocence in his murder, and a measure more through his brother's assassination. Man went from a few minutes in orbit to a walk on the moon. We weathered the Bay of Pigs and the Cuban Missile Crisis. President Johnson committed the first ground troops to Vietnam. We celebrated Woodstock, we mourned My Lai. We captured Manson, we elected Nixon. We planted the seeds of the seventies.

The harvest was bitter. In the seventies we carried the murderous solutions of Vietnam to the campus of Kent State. The White House hired "plumbers" who led us through a labyrinth to Nixon's resignation. We launched the heaviest bombings in history and lost a war. We lost our mobility in an Arab oil embargo. Women and gay people arose to demand liberation and met their determined foes in Schlafly and Bryant. We yielded the Panama Canal and opened the trans-Alaska pipeline. We celebrated a Bicentennial and elected Carter. We fled the unseen terrors of Three Mile Island and watched the "spiritual" commit murder in Guyana. We saw gay men and lesbians march in Washington. We questioned our confidence. We feared the future.

Unlike previous eras through which Wesley, Carl, Billy, and Robert lived, these two decades were probably experienced less immediately. By the sixties, these were men with established careers, set patterns of love and sex, and the experience to manage—or to even be bored by—what happened to them and their friends. They reached the condition called maturity.

259

These four narrators lived relatively quiet lives through these years and, when these interviews ended, ranged in age between sixty-four and seventy-three.

Like most people deeply involved in a profession or career, each tended to stay concentrated within the world in which he worked and to respond to his larger world only when it seized his attention in some dramatic way, as the Depression, the Second World War, and the McCarthy era had. No such upheavals occurred during these two decades, so these men were absorbed and fulfilled by composing, designing, administering, and acting.

While the four narrators talked at length about love affairs, work, finances, friends, and other matters, only two events were able to badly disturb their calm: Teddy died, and Wesley Ober fell in love with a much younger man. The problems of the four friends and the adjustments necessary, individually and within the group, are the focus of this last section of narratives, which is appropriate to our primary purpose of exploring how gay men of another generation lived and survived as gays.

The men were little touched by the emergence of a "gay consciousness" or a "gay community," and kept informed about both primarily through messengers in the form of younger friends. For better or worse, the four generally retained the attitudes about themselves and about being gay that they expressed earlier in these pages.

# Carl Mason

I told that chap who wrote my biography about the *Times* article that damned all us old movie composers to limbo. I could be amused by it by that time. But he picked up on my anecdote and made it sound as if I'd been exiled to England to live out my dotage, neglected and frustrated. He took that story and turned my stay abroad into a tragedy. I became some kind of musical Flying Dutchman, wandering Europe, condemned to taking any bone that was thrown my way, composing to order like some short-order cook. He was an idiot. . . .

The fact is that London was wonderful, the business back in California thrived—even without me—and it ended up being acquired by a conglomerate, which made us all a lot richer.

Poor wandering minstrel, indeed!

London was heaven after Hollywood. No pools, real sidewalks, no palm trees. I blessed the awful people who had spurred me to move. Frederich and I made friends, we bought enough antique silver to need a burglar-alarm system. We embraced the languid pace, hours over tea at the Ritz or poking through Fortnum's or Hatchard's or Harrod's. I worked when I wanted and Frederich worked for pleasure. I had no idea whether I could tolerate so much leisure. But it suited me.

The flat in London was lovely, late Georgian. Frederich freelanced with various London orchestras, and, if we could work our schedules out, I would accept work on the Continent whenever we wanted a little vacation. A lot of the work I got was from young film makers who were nostalgic about old movies and wanted scores that would evoke them, so I'd write in every style imaginable and have a great time. I was now getting single-card credit, my name alone on the screen. Warners used to lump me in the credits with makeup and set design and whatnot. (But then, not many people even got a credit. The credits today look like the telephone book. "Miss Loren's earrings by Flavio. Lassie's dish by Spode.") For the auteurs I was an artifact to be displayed.

I was now a credit to be prized. "Hey," the directors would say, "look who I found. He's not dead." I came into my own. My reputation grew, and while I'd do almost anything, I never did anything where I didn't have complete control or I felt I couldn't do well.

I loved England, but after I turned fifty-five I began to think about coming back. I was comfortable and happy in England, but I never rooted. Neither Frederich nor I had any reason to return, we just felt we might be happier. To be honest, it was mostly my doing. So we came back for a year's trial, our first trip back in thirteen years. We didn't even come back when Teddy died, though we'd planned to. No need, as it turned out.

# Billy Hicks

I wasn't going to put him on display like some stuffed fish, and they were crazy to ever think I would. You'll hear them say it, but don't you believe it.

Teddy had been in the hospital a few months earlier with liver problems. He'd been years without a drink, but there were some left-over problems. The hospital gave him a clean bill of health, and I'd never seen him looking better or more cheerful. So there wasn't the slightest hint, not the slightest.

I just woke up around three and knew. I don't know how, but I just sat up in bed and moved away from him. I didn't have to touch him or look at him. I knew he wasn't really there anymore. I don't know how long I sat on the bed looking out the window. I sat and looked out at all the new buildings they'd put up on Park since the end of the war. I could see three that I'd done a lot of work in.

We had a rule about not smoking in bed. I'd made it when Teddy had been drinking so heavily. I was afraid he'd burn us up. We did have a couple of fires. I went and sat on the chaise and lit a cigarette and looked at him. I think I talked out loud for a while, but I'm not sure, and I can't imagine what I would have said.

He was dead. I didn't think of him as "passed over" or "away," or "gone," or "lost." He was dead. That's the only word I can remember thinking, till I called Frank Campbell's to ask them what I should do. They said to call our doctor and leave things to him. He'd call the police.

I had no intention of doing what anybody else wanted done and I had no idea what Teddy would have wanted. I knew what I wanted. I wanted things done quickly.

After I called them, I thought I should make it look as if I'd

263

been sleeping in the other room. I should tidy up my side of the bed and go wrinkle the sheets on the bed in the other room. But that seemed like an act of denial and I would not deny Teddy, not now. Let them think what they wanted. Anyway, it was true. We'd shared a bed for almost thirty years. It would have been thirty years in another month.

The doctor came and then the police and then the Campbell people to remove the body. All very easy. They knew their business.

I sat for a while and then I called Carl in London. I didn't call Wesley or Robert. They would have wanted to do something and there was nothing to do. I told Carl, because I needed someone else to know.

I went and changed the bed, to have something to do, and then I sat and thought for a while. I thought about a funeral and decided not to do it. By now, almost everyone knew that Teddy and I were lovers, and they were always polite or kept their opinions to themselves. The extra bedroom had never fooled a soul. But a funeral was something else.

I wouldn't take the chance. I wouldn't have a funeral and take the chance that some of our straight friends wouldn't come— would snub it—or the chance that those who did come would be condescending. I knew that if anyone did or said anything and I took it wrong—or right—I would never speak to them again. I'd loved Teddy and I wouldn't expose that to a snub or a crude smirk.

I called Campbell's and told them that there would be no service of any kind and they were to proceed with cremation arrangements. I just told them to go ahead as quickly as they could. That was my right as executor. And no, I said, no urn, no ashes.

Then I called Wesley and told him that Teddy was dead and asked him to call Robert and tell him. I lied to him. I said I had not decided on arrangements. When Campbell's called to say that the cremation would take place later that day, I called Wesley and told him what I'd decided. Or course, Wesley had to say, "What about Teddy's friends?" I said, "Well, what the fuck about them?" and hung up.

Wesley and Robert stewed for a long time about the way I did things. Well, Teddy was my lover, not theirs. I did it to suit me. I suppose I did things to keep from feeling pain, though I can't

remember feeling much of anything all through that time . . .
certainly nothing that precise.

The pain came later, when I'd be shopping and see something
I knew Teddy would like or when I'd go grocery shopping and
see something dumb like shredded wheat and remember that
he'd eated that almost every morning for as long as I'd known
him. Teddy left the damnedest lot of holes in my life.

# Robert Regal

I handled Teddy's affairs, so I went ahead and did what was necessary. When we'd drawn up his will, he had no idea where any of his relatives might be, so when he passed on we had to advertise in local papers. No one ever came forward, so the estate was handled as Teddy had wished. It took the usual year or so. I can't comment on the disposition of assets. As to other relevant matters, I feel that, even after so long a time, it would be better if I didn't comment.

I felt his loss deeply. One doesn't lose a friend of over thirty years without giving a lot of thought to what was experienced. In a way I've never wholly understood, Teddy was a kind of counterbalance in my life. I can be hard on myself. I admit it. Teddy never was. Teddy could help me be a little more gentle with myself, but Teddy's affections were always clear and visible with everyone.

Just look around this room. It's pretty much as he decorated it when he lived here during the war. Teddy's sense of a home was very different from his sense of dress. I can afford to live anywhere. I stay here because it suits me. I don't stay here, as you may have heard, because I'm sentimental. I've always felt his decoration was a gift to me. He wasn't a great reader, yet he put bookshelves up two walls. I filled them. He put a wing chair with a good reading light over there. He put in a good, large desk with a comfortable chair over by the window. Those weren't things he needed. They were done for me and they have always suited me. Why spend money to change things when they are more than suitable. Besides, no matter what I spent these days, it wouldn't be half so well made.

And if they do remind me of Teddy, what's so terrible about that.

# Wesley Ober

I remember it was a Friday night that Teddy died, because I had two shows the next day. I had a new lady friend, Vera, and we were on Broadway in a really delightful thing about industrial spying in the fashion business. A wonderful comedy. We ran for almost two years.

When Billy called, I wanted to go right over, but he wouldn't hear of it. So I called Robert, as Billy asked. He didn't want me to come over and I didn't want to be alone, so I went over to Vera's.

It all seems so long ago. Billy just had Teddy whisked off the face of the earth, as if he'd never been there. There was nothing any of us could do but accept it. But somehow I never feel someone's dead till I've seen them at the funeral parlor. I seem to need evidence. Is that macabre?

I must say, when Billy decides to move he goes like a bat out of hell. Within two months he'd sold the apartment on Park, and within another month he'd bought the townhouse. He just emptied the apartment into Parke-Bernet and sold the lot. He gave the odds and ends to people in his office. Teddy had willed me four lovely French chairs, and he left Robert his huge collection of malachite. Robert never has anyone over, so I've never seen the malachite again. Billy left nothing of the past, not so much as a knife and fork. Billy had to completely restore the insides of that townhouse he bought, and when he got that organized, he surprised the hell out of me by asking me if I'd like to go around the world with him as his guest.

When he asked, my show was near the tag end of its run and we were on what are called twofers. We were one of the first shows to use those things, and I winced every time I went to my dry cleaners and saw those awful little tickets that enabled

someone to see me at a discount. I felt I'd been marked down.
Over twenty-five years in the theater and I could now be seen at
half price.

I wasn't up for anything else, so I told Vera I was leaving as
soon as the show closed. She got a little shirty about my going
off, because we'd talked about going to her place on the Cape for
a while when we closed. Come to think of it, the lady got very
shirty and told me that she might well be in rehearsal for a new
show before I was back, and would have to look into finding
another leading man. That gave me pause, but only pause. I was
fifty-seven by then, and the lady had the appetites of a
seventeen-year-old. So I thought about her ultimatum and told
her to find herself a new boy, emphasizing "boy." I suggested she
should move on to mother roles—mothers with lots of sons.
Damned if she didn't.

The trip wasn't all pleasure, at least not for Billy. We went
down to New Zealand, where he set up some kind of manufacturing arrangement for decorative moldings or some such. We
went to Japan, where he contracted for several million yards of
fabric, and then to Thailand for silks, and so on and so on
around the world.

And all along the way, Billy bought things for the new
townhouse. He'd measured every inch of the place, and when
he'd see something he was interested in he'd get out his little
book to see if it would fit. I'd never known why he'd been so
immensely successful. I saw on that trip.

We ended up in London about eight months later, our last
stop. That's where Billy told me about Teddy's will. It was
something he and Teddy had decided when they were drawing
up their wills.

Lily had left a trust for Teddy, and Teddy had done all that
business about the Gusmin Memorial and what-all—Teddy said
she would have called it the Gusmin Memorial Drunk Tank, so
we did—but Robert had run the extra money the trust produced
into a nice little account all on its own. Teddy'd left that for me in
another trust account. It was no fortune, but it gave me
something of an edge, a little independence. I cried like a baby
when Billy told me, which is probably why he waited till we were
alone in our suite at the Ritz. That money's made all the
difference, I can tell you.

When I recovered myself, I told Billy that Teddy had
probably done it because he knew I was falling apart. Teddy had

gone with me to the dentist when they'd pulled them all and
shoved in a full set of choppers. And he'd been with me—I
couldn't face it alone—when I'd gone to what is charmingly
called a corsetière to be fitted. All the damned corsets do is shove
your tummy up around your tits. What an awful day it was,
being measured and poked at like a prize sow. Teddy knew what
it meant to me, how I felt.

And the stage makeup gets thicker right along with the
middle, and you take to squinting at mirrors or get a face lift.
You stand backstage and wish the lights were brighter. And you
start to feel foolish playing men twenty years younger and hope
to God that the play's lines don't specify your age, or that there's
nothing gymnastic to do.

I didn't mind never being above the title. There was a good
steady living for me among the "featured players," and that's all
I'd ever expected—or worked for, for that matter. But the life
does begin to wear your edges off. Teddy's kindness would mean
that I wouldn't have to say yes when good sense and dignity
would make me want to say no. I could get a "four-week out" on
any show I signed for and I didn't have to be shy about insisting
on "house seats" in my contract. All little things, but they all
count. They're part of the theater's status system. That's how
much difference that bit of regular money meant to me.

How do you say thank you for something like that? Although
I'm glad Teddy never told me about it.

There's a beautiful little Inigo Jones church in Covent
Garden. St. Paul's Covent Garden. It's an actors' church. The
back of it faces the garden. Shaw used it in the opening scene of
*Pygmalion.* If you walk around the block you can find the gate
that leads into the prettiest little park, and through it there's the
entrance to the church. Inside the church are little brass plaques
commemorating actors. There's one for Vivien Leigh, one for
Ivor Novello, dozens of actors. Almost two hundred years'
worth. I went to see the rector and paid for a plaque for Teddy
and for an annual service to be said in his name. I lied. I said that
Teddy had been a distinguished American character actor. I
didn't know whether they'd let him in otherwise.

I've never told Billy. I hope he doesn't mind.

# Carl Mason

New York seemed shabby to us after so long. Most of the glitter seemed to be gone, but the vitality was still there. It was thirty years since I'd lived there. I suppose some changes were to be expected.

I hired a press agent to get the word around that I planned to be in town for several months. That didn't produce much except a lot of calls from old associates bringing me up to date on who was dead or tottering to the grave. CBS called with a project and I went over to talk to them about it. Nothing definite. Frederich signed in with the musicians' union and started getting a few calls. He preferred chamber work and went out to find some. Those aren't union jobs.

We'd taken a sublet up in the East 70's, and I signed us up for opera and concert series; we opened bank accounts, found a cook, opened charge accounts. We went to the theater twice a week for quite a while, just to catch up. We just settled in, looked up old friends, made a few new ones.

But so much was so different. One didn't linger in the theater district anymore. No more leisurely suppers and strolls on Broadway. One got in and got out. I don't like being propositioned by men or women. One didn't stroll on Fifth Avenue at night. Who wants to look at banks and airline offices—that's what had taken over. Central Park was out of bounds, the Village was charmless, Chelsea grubby.

I knew things would be different. They were in London. We had Carnaby Street and Kings Road, where all that business of long hair and bizarre clothes and drugs and psychedelic art began. When it started there, it all seemed to be in a spirit of fun, and we'd go up there and have a good time. That whole movement seemed more an act of aggression by the time we

273

came back to its American equivalent. Here, I was told it was "meaningful," but no one ever said of what. They'd made lack of discipline and addiction into virtues, because they said it was all part of an antiwar movement.

I found the music particularly disturbing, because so much of it was formless and chaotic. I admired the electronics and the sophisticated arrangements, but the shapeless rage of it left me wondering. The lyrics were that awful kind of pseudo-folk, when one could understand them, and those seemed to depend for their rhyme schemes on mispronouncing words. To be sure, there were Bernstein and Sondheim and Bock & Harnick, but they were out of the mainstream. The scream of rage was with us. It was as if Bacon gave up painting and wrote songs.

And I have just shown my age. Well, it is my age.

After a while, I began to be glad that we'd committed ourselves to only a year. I wasn't sure I liked America anymore. But then the CBS project did come through and I said yes, more out of a need to work than a deep interest in the thing. It turned out to be one of those Neilsen wonders that surprise everyone, so I was again a star in my business. I still don't think my score was nearly as good as many I've done, but it was attached to a big hit, so I rode along on the show's success. I think it was that more than anything that kept us here. I must say, Frederich seemed to enjoy the city more than I did. He had no memories of it.


Oh, for God's sake, don't go asking us questions like that. And don't explain, you'll just make it worse. I know what your question means. You can ask me about what I've learned from my long life, you can call me mature instead of old, but what you're really asking is how it feels to be an old crock.

Don't ask us that kind of thing. If you're lucky, you'll get older. Answer the question for yourself. Being old doesn't *mean* anything. I don't know a whit more than I did. I know less, and if anything, that's a comfort. Just take your silly question and go home, and don't forget you're coming to dinner with us next Sunday. Seven sharp!

# Billy Hicks

Wesley wanted me to stay at his place when we got back, but I told him that I'd check into the Berkshire. It was near the office and the new house. He'd been the best companion I could have had. He didn't avoid talking about Teddy, but he seemed to be able to avoid talking about anything that might have made me sad.

After I checked into the hotel, I walked over to the house to see how the work was coming along. I'd left a very good woman in charge of things, so when I got there the work was complete, except for the painting and papering.

The minute I walked in I knew that it was going to be beautiful when I finished. I'd had everything shipped to my receiving agent, so there was literally nothing in the house. I could enjoy the architecture just for itself. It would be a whole new life. It would be a complete departure from the past, from everything I'd known with Teddy. Well, there was a kicker in all that. While I was walking around the house I began to cry, and I didn't even notice till I heard myself sobbing. I was on the second floor, so I just went and sat in the corner of the bedroom and cried. A workman found me there next morning, very out of it. He didn't have any idea who I was, so he called the police, and they found my identification, called an ambulance, and got hold of my office. I'd apparently had a nervous breakdown.

Robert came by the hospital and looked agitated. Well, I suppose that's not surprising, since I was in the nut ward. He said that he'd go by my offices and meet with my executive staff and serve as a kind of liaison for us all. Not that I could have decided anything tougher than blowing my nose. Wesley came by with the biggest goddamned basket of fruit I've ever seen. But he had the good sense not to try and cheer me up. He looked

275

after personal things for me. He called friends, saw to my mail, brought me some good gossip.

After several months with a very kind psychotherapist, I went back to work. But every day I'd walk into my office past all those dozens of people who worked for me and wonder what the hell they were all up to. The company had grown very big, and even though I'd been out of things for over a year, it had gone ticking right along. It was a lesson I'd sooner not have learned. Me, expendable? Never!

I was only forty-nine or so. At first I thought I'd start a new division, but I couldn't think of an area we weren't already in, and I found that every time I thought of all the work that meant I'd get this feeling of complete exhaustion. My shrink helped me understand that.

I started rationing myself to half-days at the office. There was no way I could go broke. And wonder of wonders, the company kept right on going and the annual report showed bigger profits. Hard to admit, but the company had a life of its own.

I tried the Jamaica-Palm Beach-Hamptons circuit for a while, but that wasn't much fun. The only thing I liked about it was that I was the youngest person around. But by the time I'd get back to town, I felt as old as that lot was. Worse yet, I started feeling as old as I was.

The odd young man came and went at the house, and that was pleasant. I didn't want anything permanent. They were nice to have around while they were around. A few had some talent, and I was able to help here and there. I found they were a nice way to stay in touch with what was going on, and I learned the Twist, which I was convinced was very good for the hips. Elsa Maxwell said it was. I hadn't learned anything since the Jitterbug.

There's always some young man or other around. It's nice. They get me out to discos and the trendy restaurants and talk me into buying cowboy boots I never wear and get me out to the Pines. It's all great fun. I love being the dirty old man with all the money.

# Robert Regal

I'm busy enough with my own affairs. That Presidential advisory committee takes more time than it should, considering how little of our advice they follow. I was appalled by government waste when I worked in Washington for the OPA. If possible, it's even worse today.

I had no idea what to make of Wesley. We all just assumed he'd keep right on going from one person to another. An alliance with only one person didn't seem to be at all his style. Billy made a life with one person for thirty years and Wesley made thirty alliances in the same time. Now Billy goes hopping about like a teen-ager and Wesley settles down, or whatever it's called. As I said at the time, if Wesley insists on proving there's no fool like an old fool, that's up to him, I suppose.

I've never understood the lot of them, and there's no reason I should start now.

# Wesley Ober

I'd gone into Chock Full O' Nuts for a sandwich. I've always loved their nutted cream cheese on raisin bread. Anyway, I glanced up and saw this man. I didn't want to stare, but I was struck by something. I thought what an awfully good-looking man he'd be if he took better care of himself. I was thinking about him, so I looked up again and saw that I'd been looking in a mirror. I'd seen myself. It's not that I mind encountering the great eternal verities, but I'd prefer not to do it in Chock Full O' Nuts. I thought things like that happened on mountain tops with heavenly choirs on the soundtrack.

To be sure, I still looked good . . . just less good.

You see, it wasn't supposed to happen to me. I was never going to get old, and there I was a fast sixty. Well, almost.

Actually, my birthday was the following week, and Billy was giving me a party, about which I had very mixed feelings. I also felt that they were all taking a kind of malicious delight in announcing to all our friends that I was over the hill. Hill, hell! I was over an alp. Billy said that when he carried my cake in, he wasn't going to sing "Happy Birthday." He was going to sing "The Old Gray Mare." I told him I hoped he looked good in cake.

I planned to go to the party after a day of facial massage and assorted treatments, and when they made their awful jokes about "getting on in years," I'd joke right back. Still, I wandered around regretting that I'd never lied about my age.

The party was one of Billy's specials, and Estelle's car was going to pick me up first and then we'd swing by and get her.

Estelle was my current "lady," as they're now called. A widow lady, actually. Her husband had been one of the great theater writers. He'd been dead for quite a while, but his plays got done and done and done. There were constant first-class revivals all

279

over the world, and Estelle was always running off somewhere to receive some honor in his memory. Within one month, the Royal Shakespeare Company did one, and a month later Britain's National Theatre did another, and then she went on to Munich, where they did the one about the newspaper business. They turned his plays into musicals, into television specials, and one even became a successful TV series. They were an annuity. Estelle didn't need an annuity.

Numerically, Estelle was seventh in a string of very nice women who seemed to keep coming into my life. They were always attached to the theater, and we always seemed to be able to put together some kind of arrangement that suited us both. To be clearer, we shared a bed from time to time, but we were always free.

I liked having the gals around, because I liked parties and it was nice to be asked as a couple. No one was really fooled by these arrangements, but most people had something of the kind going on, so they turned it all into a little harmless gossip: I won't get stuffy about your whips if you'll lay off my hookers. That kind of thing.

When I wasn't with Estelle, I was still a desirable guest. Max Beerbohm said that the world is divided into only two groups, guests and hosts. I was a good guest. I was on *Vogue*'s list of "ten most desirable male guests" four years running. That, dear boy, is the Oscar of the catering circuit.

With one exception, my ladies and I parted amicably enough when the time came and kept in touch and stayed friends. I even got out of a show and flew out to Hollywood when Sheila had her stroke. I stayed with her till she got back on her feet. Poor baby was ashamed to have me see her. The stroke got the right side of her face. Even with her hair draped down the side, she couldn't hide it. Sad sight. She deserved better. After she got used to having me around, I told her to get her face out where I could see it and to stop turning away every time I came into her room. I told her, "You're going to have to look at someone and you're going to have to learn to talk again. If you don't work, you'll die." She tried like hell. To tell the truth, it's no pleasure watching someone slobber or listen to them burble out their words, but that's the way it was. She got back almost all the use of her body. I used to get her laughing by telling her that she'd not only act again, she'd fuck again. She'd laugh and make

the most awful noise. She's still around on television. Can't kill
those old dames with a stick.

Anyway, Estelle was the latest, and she was going with me to
my birthday party. While we were sitting in back of her
limousine on the way to Billy's, I thought, "Well, if you've got to
head into senility, this is doing it in style."

Billy threw a huge affair—there must have been eighty people.
The guest list was "glittering," as the *Times* said.

Everybody was hugging everybody, so I hugged Robert,
which made him break out in a cold sweat. Estelle said I was
being mean.

Now here comes the big dramatic moment. Carl and
Frederich came in with one of the most dazzling young men I'd
ever seen. I knew the minute I saw him that he was either a model
or actor. Nobody else stands that way, always aiming at the key
light. He was wasting his time, because he didn't *have* a bad
angle. When Carl told me he was in *Hair*, I just nodded.

I've rarely been shy, but that young man made me feel very
unsure of myself. He was attentive to the birthday boy, but I was
intimidated by him. I'd been on the make, too. I knew the pitch.

It was two or so when the car dropped me off at my
apartment, and I was tired, so I was irritated when I got through
the door and the phone was ringing. It was Craig, the young man
at the party. He was in a phone booth on my corner and wanted
to come up. I almost said no, but I said yes, and it was one of the
worst nights of my life.

At sixty, one likes to be ready for a gentleman caller.

I shouldn't try and make it funny. Actually, I was in a panic.
You see, for the past few years, if I had a liaison—Jesus, I'm
sounding like Robert. Let me start again.

For the last few years my tricks had been either hustlers or a
few numbers from the old days. They suited me fine: no
romance, no staying over, nothing too exhausting. And I
always knew when they were to arrive, which gave me time to
arrange myself, so to speak. I'd have time to get undressed and
arrange the bedroom lights, like some kind of Colette heroine
who's reached the age of high collars and pink scarves over the
lampshades. I'd meet my guest in the darkened hall and see him
in. I wore a very full velvet robe. Then, while they were
undressing, I'd drop my robe and hop into bed. I didn't like my
body anymore. I'd look at it and think, You need ironing.

Did you see *A Little Night Music*? An older man has married a very young woman, who succeeds in remaining a virgin after the wedding. He sings about himself and there's a line that goes, "My body's all right, but not in perspective and not in the light." The audience laughed at the line, while I just sat there nodding in agreement.

Craig was on his way up and, God help me, I wanted him. He was beautiful and I wanted him, even though I knew he had calculating eyes and that there was a price tag on him as surely as there was on any of those young men the service sent.

Craig finally rang the bell and I opened the door, and he stepped in and kissed me. He wasn't treading on virgin territory, but I went wobbly. He kept on kissing me and I kept thinking, "This is crazy and I should get him out." But he said, "Let's go to bed," and I was too greedy to be sensible.

Well, he went to bed and I went into the bathroom. I hid the little telltale blue plastic box that holds my false teeth at night and I got out of my corset. I made the mistake of looking at myself in the mirror. The corset always left a reddish imprint around my middle. Every time I unwrapped myself I thought I looked as if I'd been made of wicker—the Wickerwork Man of Oz. There was a seed or something under my denture and they were beginning to bother me, and I was starting to cry. I couldn't expose myself to that beautiful boy. I couldn't let him put his tongue in my mouth and feel that plastic stuff that covered the roof of my mouth. I couldn't turn my head away from him and let him see the scars behind my ears from the lift.

I've no idea how long I was in there, but he called, "Where are you?" and I yelled back, "Go home. Just go home."

He came into the bathroom and found me in my robe, sitting on the edge of the tub and crying. He never asked what was the matter. He just sat down next to me and put his arm around me until I calmed down.

I finally told him that my trouble was I wanted to be as young as he was. I wanted to be young again. I didn't want to be an old ruin with a lot of spare parts. Jesus, all I needed was a glass eye.

We went to bed because he wanted to and because I was exhausted by that time. He held me and soothed me, and I worried about the price.

We didn't make love until the next morning, and when we did it was extraordinary. It was as lovely as I remembered it being with Bernard in Catch Mills when I was a kid. That told me a lot I'd sooner not have known.

He called every day after that and kept saying he wanted to see me. I made up a lot of stories, and he told me he *would* see me again, so all I was doing was delaying things.

Have you ever made up your mind not to think about something? Then you know how successful that is.

I wouldn't think of Craig. I wouldn't think of him all the time.

I remember not liking *The Blue Angel* because I thought the Emil Jannings character was a silly old poop who deserved everything that happened to him. There was that old fool chasing after that German dumpling with fat thighs, and I hadn't the foggiest idea why he didn't pull himself together and just walk away. I didn't understand obsession, because I'd never wanted anything that much.

I had a lunch date with Robert a few days later. Robert is not the kind of person in whom I confided, but he was handy that day and I was beside myself by then. I'd never been in love, and I had the awful feeling that I might be. I was too old for the grand passion. I still had a career to think about, my friends, Estelle, a lot of things. I thought I stood to lose a lot and I couldn't think of one thing I'd be gaining. Life was very good as it was. Adding Craig to it could make it a mess.

Robert listened to my whole spiel and then said, "Do you feel you use Estelle?" I was outraged by his question, till I understood it. Estelle bought my clothes, took me on trips for months at a time, gave me entrée to any home in New York, or Palm Beach for that matter, and I never once felt that I'd used her. She didn't do anything for me I couldn't do for myself. I let her because she liked taking care of me.

I told Robert, "Of course I don't use her." He said, "Then what makes you think he'll use you? Besides," he said, "what makes you think this is the love of your life?" I said, "It is," and he said, "I hope not."

When Craig called again I made a date to see him. A date! At my age, a date.

Joe Allen's was a new spot then, a kind of poor man's Sardi's. It was lively, and we met there after he finished in *Hair*. He knew all the chorus people in Joe's and I knew all the character actors. That said a lot to me. When we'd finished our dinners, he said, "We're going back to your place now." I thought he might say something like that, and I had a line ready that I'd been rehearsing since he called. I was simply going to say, "I'm too old for you." I fixed him with a very stern, no-nonsense look and said firmly, "You're too old for me." He roared and I felt like an idiot. If I'd read my line right, it might have ended right there. I felt so silly that all my arguments were shot. He won that round. We went home.

He was charming, he was young, he was beautiful, he had talent, and he pursued me and I couldn't believe it. I didn't feel lucky, I felt afraid.

I didn't want to see *Hair*, but he insisted, so I took Estelle, who didn't want to see it either. Estelle was raised in Canada by Victorian parents, and this new kind of theater usually left her affronted and confused. Of course, we had house seats right down center in the orchestra. When a lot of the cast disrobed onstage I was startled. Estelle was genuinely shocked. Craig was one of the naked ones. He looked beautiful, and I realized that something awful had happened. I didn't want all those people gawking at him. He was mine. I didn't want to share him.

Have you ever been jealous? It's awful. It's unreasoning and destructive, and it went right to my stomach. It gave me the runs. Jealousy added a terrible burden to what I was already feeling, and I wanted to go someplace and hide. I didn't want all those feelings. I played a character once who was going through something of the same thing. He says, "I feel like I'm going sixty miles an hour and I want to jump, because I know that's safer than staying where I am." I jumped.

It was off-season, and I wasn't working just then, so I talked Estelle into a month in Mexico. I started avoiding Craig again. I stayed home a lot and stewed and sat on the john. He'd sounded irritated on the phone, but I wasn't sure it wasn't just acting. He must want something. The afternoon of the day before we were to leave, he called and I told him I was going out of town for a month. He said he was coming right over and I said he shouldn't.

He did, of course. I let him in but I couldn't look at him. He wanted to know what I was afraid of. I suppose I was feeling safe because I'd be far away in a few hours, so I told him that I was falling in love with him and I didn't want to. I didn't want to take the chance that I'd be used, I didn't want all those feelings, and I didn't want to feel jealous or worry that he'd still be young when

I was using a wheelchair. I told him all that, everything I was afraid to say. If someone had said all that to me, I'd have left. He just sat there. I finally told him to get the hell out so I could have a good cry. I think I yelled at him.

He finally got up, but he went into the bedroom and just stayed in there.

I sat down. I was awfully tired. In all my life, I'd let people go when they were ready or I'd leave when I was. Never any fuss. I'd gotten to sixty without fuss. I sat there and knew that the person I wanted most in the world was in my bedroom. All I had to do was move. But that would take so much energy. I tried to outlast him. I thought that if I could sit there long enough he'd get up and go. I sat there and really prayed for God to send him away and leave me in peace.

I finally went. I went into the bedroom and took off my corset right in front of him. I hoped he'd be as repelled as I was ashamed. He just sat and watched me. He didn't seem to notice that I was defying him to want me. Well, we made love.

Later, I woke him up so he could go to the theater. He got up and dressed and I just lay there. He came over and kissed me and said, "I want you to write to me." He seldom asked for anything. He just told me what he wanted. "Write to me." "I'm coming over." "Take me to the movies." "Come meet me." Well, why not.

I went to the door with him and said, "I love you," and he said, "Good," and left.

Estelle and I flew off the next morning. I'd finally surrendered, and I felt wonderful about that and terrible about leaving him. We went to Mexico City, which I've always loved, and so did Estelle. We had a lot of friends there, and in Cuernevaca, so we were going all the time. I found some time almost every day to write Craig. I was in love and I was starting to enjoy it. I even started planning our future. I was going to play Henry Higgins. I would see that he got voice lessons with Fanny Bradshaw and acting classes with Hagen or Strasberg. I would introduce him to Alfred and Lynney and Helen and Noël and every name I thought worth dropping. I would take him to Shields for shirts and Dunhill for suits. To paraphrase Henry Higgins, I would heap the treasures of my Miltonic mind on the guttersnipe. I would do everything I was afraid he wanted me to do.

Of course, I had to try all of that to find out he didn't give a

damn about any of it. He didn't want to get out of his dungarees
or army jackets. He didn't want to meet Noël Coward, he
wanted to meet Marlon Brando. I felt awful. If he didn't want
what I had to give, what the hell was he doing with me? Far be it
from me to accept the obvious.

And if he couldn't meet Brando, he'd settle for the Beatles, all
four of them. I didn't understand him. I'd been crazy about the
Boswell Sisters, but I never cared to meet them, or the Mills
Brothers, for that matter.

Well, if I wasn't going to play Henry Higgins, who could I
play? I tried several Spencer Tracy roles on for size and got no
cooperation from Craig. I tried being very "elder statesman," all
compassionate understanding, until Craig asked me why I kept
using "that funny voice." I tried being the boulevardier, with
absolutely no success. Most of the time I felt like a cross between
Medea and King Lear, just another daffy jealous queen
screaming in the wilderness. I described myself to Carl that way
and he just nodded yes. You see, I couldn't see myself as the
young swain. I'd always known who I was, and when I didn't I
could fake it, fall into some role and get through.

Every time I struck some pose, Craig would laugh at me, or
mimic me, which was even worse.

My friends took a very jaundiced view of the whole affair.
Carl told me that one couldn't get too early a start on second
childhood. Billy said it served me right, which I never did
understand, and Robert just looked pruny. I was always grateful
that none of that lot took up theater criticism.

Well, anyway, I was happy when I wasn't too confused or
jealous or crazy. Craig just moved into my life and stayed there.

I finally got used to having him around and started behaving
naturally. My friends came to like Craig or to at least accept
him, grudgingly at first. I was careful not to introduce him to
Estelle, but she noticed that I wasn't available all the time, as I
had been when I wasn't in a show.

Of course, when my friends started being comfortable with
Craig, I became jealous of them all. I was sure that each of them
was after Craig. If they joked with him, I was sure it was a pass.
If they asked us to dinner, I was sure it was because they wanted
to be near Craig. I think it's called paranoia. All that nonsense
would go through my head and I'd listen to it and say to myself,
"You're crazy, you've gone stark staring."

But time cooled me down and I started thinking that I had entirely too much time to think about myself—and about Craig—so I put myself out for work. I pestered my agent until he got me some readings.

Craig got offered a role in an off-Broadway play and decided to leave *Hair*. He'd been with it for nine months and was bored to death. He wasn't part of the original cast, and he had nothing to gain by staying with the show. I agreed. He should be doing a lot of different roles at his age. I read the play he'd been offered and thought it very good. I told him to accept.

He loved acting and worked hard. He apparently took direction without complaint, and when he talked to me about the show he sounded like a complete pro, a good sign. That pleased me. Early on, I'd run lines with him, and I was happy to see that the play held up and got better with every reading. And he read well. All good signs. If the production was good, it could do very nice things for his career.

I took my agent—call him Pat—to opening night. Craig had third billing and he was working with some awfully good people I knew either from their work or by reputation. It was a wonderful play and very well directed, and Craig was awful. He'd read well with me, but he washed out on stage. He was even technically bad. He swallowed the ends of lines and his gestures never matched up with what he was saying . . . like Nixon. He was awkward and amateurish, and my heart went out to him.

I thought that perhaps I was being too demanding because of my own ego. I wanted so much to be proud of him. Before I went backstage I asked Pat what he thought. He asked me if I wanted the truth, and I told him I certainly did. Pat was kind and sensible. He said he'd been around too long to dismiss any talent on the basis of one performance, but that Craig lacked so much in basic technique that it was hard to tell.

I'd always been able to go backstage and tell the most outrageous lies to friends. You know the kind of thing: Darling, I was simply swept off my feet. You've never been better or prettier—or handsomer—or whatever.

Oh God, how I didn't want to go backstage. I wanted to lie to Craig—and knew I'd botch it. I didn't know what to do, so I asked Pat. "Well," he said, "if he loves the theater, tell him to get to work. If you want to help, get him to the best people."

I decided to split the difference. I would lie backstage and save the truth for later, when I'd had a chance to do a bit of scripting. I wasn't going to damage his ego for anything in the world, but I didn't want him to go pointlessly on telling everyone he was an actor and never working or working on junk. I'd seen too much of that in my time.

But when you come right down to it, who was I to be ladling out that kind of judgment? I don't know how to make this clear. Most actors go into the business because they love it. Not *love* like "I love that hat" or "I loved that show," but love the way a lot of people love power or money. You don't show up at nine in the morning for the salary, you give your life to it. To my loss, I never did, so I never went much beyond being an able journeyman. But I knew the goods when I saw it, and I saw it often and I knew what it cost the people who did it. I think acting may be the toughest and worst bargain a person can make in life. If you make that bargain, there's often no way out. I've watched people leave the business, and the luster goes off them, their souls become cautious. And if you think I'm being too dramatic, get to know some actors.

I prayed for conviction to make lying to Craig convincing, but I didn't get it.

I went backstage and used an evasion. I said, "It was wonderful to see you up there. You looked terrific." And we all went off to the cast party to wait for the reviews: I didn't stay till they came in. I told Craig to get drunk or high or whatever and to have a wonderful time. I fled. I felt like Judas.

The show came off pretty well, but Craig was slaughtered by the reviewers. I don't remember the adjectives, but they were harsh. It was after two when he called me in tears. I told him to come along and I'd give him a drink he obviously didn't need.

When he got there I was surprised to see that he wasn't nearly as drunk as I'd thought. So I sat him down and decided to get him really pissed.

But I wasn't going to get off with a drink and a pat on the head. He asked me if I'd tell him the truth about his performance. I honestly told him I wasn't sure I could or even should, and I could see him stiffen. Well, I thought, "In for a penny, in for a pound."

I brought him a drink and sat near him. I started with the longest, most rambling preamble you've ever heard, and he knew I was dodging. I knew he knew, so I stopped and started again. I told him that I wanted to help him get the best help possible, people to work with him, so that he could work on his voice and technique. I told him I didn't know how much talent he had. I knew he had the dedication. I finally told him that he hadn't held his own on that stage that night.

And he said, "And I suppose all that work you want me to do will make me a great star and brilliant actor like you?" He said, "If I get to act like you after forty years, I don't want it."

That hurt some—that hurt a lot—but I let it go. He went on about my acting, until I had to tell him to shut up.

He wanted to fight with me. I didn't have the heart for it. I'd told him the truth, I'd taken a terrible chance and lost. I told him that, and that he'd have to make what he wanted of it, but he must never ask me for the truth again, if all he wanted was some goddamned lie that could damage any chance he had to become good.

He told me to go fuck myself and who did I think I was and that I could shove it, and he left.

I sat there feeling lousy and wishing I'd lied even if he hadn't believed it.

There were several weeks of silence after that.

They managed to get another week out of the show, but there was paper for it everywhere. Sad. It was a good play, but that was one of those seasons when, if it wasn't British and it was serious, you could forget it. We didn't know any of the same people, so I didn't hear a word about Craig. I eventually got a card from Florida that simply said, "I'm here for a while," and was signed with just his initials.

I cried a lot and my friends got heartily fed up with my carrying on. I was very grateful for Estelle and the parties, and I went back to being with her a lot of the time. I read for some more shows and actually went into rehearsal for one until their backing dried up. I did a lot of entertaining and had people by two or three times a week, mostly actors, with some friends mixed in. I've always needed a lot of people around. I think it's because I grew up in a large family. Carl says it's because I need an audience.

When I was alone in the apartment I hated it. Craig had given me a hi-fi, on which he constantly played stuff I couldn't stand, and when that wasn't on, the television he'd talked me into buying was going. I'd never much liked radio, and I was afraid I liked television too much. I liked game shows. The more awful something was the more I seemed to like it, so I never turned it on. I was embarrassed by my own taste.

I finally got an offer to go out for six months with a good production of *Desk Set,* so I took it. My old chum Anita was going to star. The older ladies liked doing it. They could be romantic in it without looking silly.

I didn't get used to Craig's being gone, but I didn't stop living. It gave me time to think, not that I needed time to think about becoming sixty-one.

We were in rehearsal over at Broadway Arts when he came back. He was waiting outside the studios, and when I came out he just walked up to me and said, "Take me to dinner."

He looked awful. I didn't ask him where he'd been or what he'd been doing. In a way, it was none of my business and I didn't want it to be. It wasn't that I didn't care. By the time we'd finished dessert, I'd told him about the show and our itinerary, which was Boston, Chicago, Denver, and San Francisco, and I'd told stories about the cast. I ran out of conversation. He finally said something like "Find me the right teachers."

I was very out of touch with who was a good teacher, so I told him that he was in a better position to find good teachers than I was, but that I'd help him in every way possible. But he said he wanted me to tell him. I said that a lot of the young people I admired had some training at RADA, the Royal Academy of Dramatic Arts in London. And he said, "Can you help?" I said, "Maybe," because I had a lot of connections over there, and I'd even ask Estelle to help if I had to.

When we left the restaurant he said, "Take me home," and I said no. He didn't argue. I had to give him some money for a hotel, but I couldn't take him home with me. I couldn't tell if he was angry or hurt about my saying no. I didn't even know what I was feeling.

Then he scared the hell out of me by grabbing me and kissing me right on the lips in front of the restaurant. I didn't even dare look around to see who might have seen us, I just bolted off down the street. He'd kissed me in front of God and everybody and scared me. All I could think was, Maybe people thought we were Italian. Somehow I felt that half of New York had been there watching. I'd been kissed in the street, right on the lips. I'd be arrested. When I finally slowed down I started to laugh. For ne reason I felt good.

So I walked home, explaining Craig to myself for the nine-millionth time. He was out of the question. He was too young. I was too old for all the drama. When he'd just taken off I'd pulled things together again, but I swore I would not go through that again. I had no intention of being a professional old fool. Well, I'd said it all to myself so often that I was thoroughly bored with it. And it was hard to concentrate, because I kept thinking of the kiss. What would people say?

It was early when I got in, so I called around to see who was free. Billy had had a date cancel on him, so I met him at East Five Five, a classy gay restaurant where everybody gathered to show off a new costume or a new lover or some new money. Billy met me at the bar and asked me what had run over me. I told him Craig was back and he said, "And?" I said, "And nothing." I told Billy I planned to help Craig out with his studies and then I went on about my age, his age, his needs, my fears. Billy listened as long as he could and then he said, "Do it or don't, but make up your mind." I asked him what he'd do, and he said, "I'd either have some fun with it or give it up," he wouldn't agonize over it. I said I was too old, and Billy fixed me that beady eye of his and said, "No, my love, you're not as young as you want to be, and there's a difference." He finally said, "You're not going to get many more chances for anything, so I'd take it." There's home truth for you.

We got swacked and sentimental and talked about old times, which usually bores the hell out of both of us. Billy had to put me in a cab.

Craig woke me up in the middle of the night. He was crying. I don't remember him saying a thing on the phone, just crying. Well, you can guess the rest. Come home to Papa, come home to the old fool, come home to the old fart.

I finally had to ask Estelle's help to get him into RADA in midterm, but she brought it off through one of those "theater Sir" friends of hers. She was very curious about my interest in the "young man," as she constantly called him, and I was evasive enough to make her even more interested.

Craig left for England a couple of days after arrangements were complete, and that left me with three days to pack myself up for my tour. We planned to meet in England when my tour was over. I'd fly from San Francisco.

My tour ended in Denver. I came to in the Denver hospital and there was Estelle way off in the distance. She said I asked her to get Craig, and when she said she didn't know how to reach him, I apparently cursed her out for losing him. And that is how I returned to life. I'd been out for two days.

I remember running to center stage for the curtain call and that was it. Perfect blackout, till Estelle.

We were doing nice business in Denver. Anita had a following and her fans always turned out. We were all feeling the altitude and one martini worked like two. We had to rest a lot, because *Desk Set* is played at a pretty fast pace. But we were adjusting. I'd been complaining to the stage manager that he'd have to carry me on for my last scene, but I whizzed through it and stood in the wings waiting for the curtain line. It came, and I moved to my position for the call, and the curtain went up on me lying flat-out center stage. You don't need an exit line if you've got a really great bit of business. They told me that Anita was so surprised that she went right ahead and took her bow as if I weren't lying there. She had the grace to take only one bow. I almost died to do it, but I finally upstaged her.

They got me into intensive care and kept me under with drugs. Thank God it was Saturday night when it happened, because they had till Monday night to get my standby up in the part. Anita called Estelle, who flew out to make arrangements to have my body shipped back East. It was that close.

When they started cutting back on drugs and I got my wits back, I found out I'd had a heart attack and a fairly major one. Since I wasn't dead, I didn't pay much attention to the details. I think I felt a little cheated that I didn't make my final exit onstage. If you die in bed there's no drama, nothing to talk about. If you do it center stage it becomes part of the lore.

When I left intensive care, Estelle had me put into one of the hospital's best private rooms, and she saw to necessities like vodka and Pepperidge Farm cookies.

I'd been in that room a couple of days when I woke up in the middle of the night and felt that there was someone in the room. It was Craig. I asked him how he'd gotten there, and he said Carl had reached him and arranged for tickets back. I'd talked to Carl and Billy and Robert every day, and no one had said a word. I told them I planned to wait till I was out of the hospital to tell Craig.

Craig asked me how bad it was, and I told him that I was a lot 'tter and might even go back to the show in San Francisco.

That's what I'd been thinking. Craig was the fifth person who told me I was crazy.

Craig said he was going to take me back to New York and look after me, and I told him to stay a day or so and then get his ass back to RADA. He just looked at me and said, "I found out I'm not good enough." He said it was okay, that he'd actually felt relief once he knew for sure. As he said that night, he'd never worry that he hadn't given it his best try. It must have hurt like hell when he found out. He looked fine, so I didn't pursue it. He always looked the way he felt.

Estelle met Craig the next day. She couldn't have been nicer to him. When she told him that she knew he'd help me get better faster, I knew I didn't have any secrets from her. Ladies in their sixties are adaptable. The two of them would hang around my room while I had my gruel and Jell-O and then they'd go off and gorge themselves at Brown's or somewhere.

I started feeling well enough to become a pain in the ass about getting out and joining the company in San Francisco. That's when Estelle told me I was obviously well enough to be told that I'd been replaced. Estelle said it was her doing. She'd connived with Anita to remove that temptation by putting someone good in the part.

That's when Estelle told me what was going to be done. I'd be let out of the hospital to go home by train. She and Craig would travel with me. The doctors had told her that I was to do no stage work until the doctor in New York gave his approval, and she said, "Frankly, that may never be." All I could think to say was, "Oh!" She saved the best till last. Estelle said she wanted to marry me and I blurted out, "But I don't love you," and she was very annoyed and asked me what that had to do with anything, at our age. She said she'd never known a man she enjoyed more and that she wanted to take care of me. God knows she could and often did.

I told her I wanted to think about it. I still wince when I think of my end of that conversation; my lines were right out of reel five of a Betty Grable movie. Can you imagine? "I want to think about it." Heroine drops curtsy and exits.

Estelle told me to take my time, but that there was one othe thing she wanted to say. She said, "I want to marry you, but n little boys." I didn't have a line for that. She said she liked Cra but she wanted to preclude gossip and she had no intention being laughed at because her husband dallied. She knew what our crowd could say about one another. It could be pretty funny and pretty ugly. Estelle has never deserved slander.

I told her I understood. I also understood how kindly she meant her proposal. I wanted to tell her about Craig. I wanted to tell her that I loved him, but I was afraid she'd just make a sour face or, worse yet, laugh at me. Knowing her, she probably wouldn't have done either, but I was afraid.

Nothing more was ever said about the matter. I didn't say no and she didn't ask again. We stayed the best of friends. I loved her, but marriage wouldn't have done much for us. Besides, I'd kept proving I didn't want to be without Craig. I'd finally given in.

Craig left the train in Chicago and flew on ahead to New York to be sure that the apartment was in shape and that the hospital bed we'd ordered had arrived.

Craig and I settled in. He looked after me and I got well. I got up, I went shopping, I started going back to doing some entertaining, and I started wanting to work. All I was afraid of was sex. Craig kept making overtures and I'd be evasive. I wanted him badly, but I was afraid of dropping dead on him. The idea that one will pop off in mid-ejaculation puts a certain damper on ardor. I kept having visions of the whole ghastly event. I'd learned that my life was taking a fairly ironic turn. I'd faced my age in Chock Full O' Nuts, I'd had my only proposal in a hospital room, and I was sure I would die *in flagrante delicto*.

I'm happy to report Craig finally seduced me. He got me drunk, and I have absolutely no sense when I'm drunk. You'd have to be drunk to risk your life for a fuck. Of course he got to use the amyl nitrite the doctor prescribed for me.

I'd started feeling a lot better, so I tried getting some televison-commercial work. I figured they wouldn't overtax me and the extra money would be nice. I did two commercials, and I completely enjoyed making them. I just hated seeing them. In ne I was a titled Englishman, and I was next to a Russian lfhound in a two-shot as I said, "I put on the dog at the kennel because of what I put into Czar." Then the dog said, on." In the other one I was an army general bending over and saying, "Capture their appetite with Stouffers." I kidding I got. People were always quoting them to me lame jokes. They'd come to table at our apartment, 'd serve the entrée, someone would say something

like "Oh, good, Wes's famous Ralston ragoût." I decided I
could do without that kind of work.

If I was careful, Teddy's trust took care of things nicely for
both of us.

I don't know how to describe my life with Craig. It wasn't
exciting or hilarious, and there are almost no good stories. It
was actually a little humdrum and it suited me. And Craig was
happy. He lost that restless tic in his nature.

Much to everyone's surprise, Craig and I turned out to be
good for one another. However, our first Christmas together he
bought me love beads and I gave him a Sulka tie. As you can see,
there was something of a gap. But we wore one another's gifts
like good little soldiers. He took me to Fire Island that summer
and I took him to Venice and Florence. Craig got me to let my
hair grow. But I had it cut after Carl said I looked like Wallace
Beery playing Rapunzel. We both tried pot. Craig became
withdrawn and depressed, and I tried to go out our tenth-floor
window. It didn't suit us. We've been together quite a while now.
I've watched Craig go from shopping at army-surplus stores to
the Chemise Lacoste counter at Bloomingdale's. Well, it's to be
expected. He's getting older.

We adjusted to one another. My hardest adjustment was to
letting him have his little flings on the side. I didn't so much
adjust as learn to keep my trap shut. As my Ma used to say,
"Least said, soonest mended."

I'd do some traveling with Estelle in the winter, Craig and I
would go to Europe with friends in the spring or fall, and there
were usually summers at Fire Island: a good life.

I was able to buy this apartment with Robert's help—and
Estelle's. Estelle even started including Craig in some of her
parties, and I taught him which flatware was used with what.

Craig held some jobs, and he'd stay as long as he was happy in
them or until we felt like going away for a while. It was selfish of
me. I wanted him with me as much as possible. I didn't much
want to be alone. Besides, I loved the time I spent with him. My
friends didn't approve. Carl said, "You know, Craig's not
dumb." Billy said Craig should have some kind of career. Leave
it to Robert to tie the whole thing up. Robert said, "What kind
of life is he going to have after you're gone."

That was plain enough. He was right, and that got him
the anger he deserved. Robert could put up with my irrita-
tion, because he was right. I'd seen it often enough in New

York. There was that movie executive who'd been living with a lover for over thirty years when he died. In less than a day the family moved in and the lover was on the street. They even kept his clothes. I'd seen a lot of variations on that story.

But I didn't want my friends to be right. I was being selfish, but that's never stopped me. I wanted my time with Craig. We'd lived together six years by then.

Robert and Billy worked out a scheme. The trust Teddy had left me couldn't be touched, but it could make investments if they looked safe. So Billy said he would open a retail outlet for his products and Robert would partially finance it from the trust. Some kind of stock setup. Craig would manage it and be given a salary and a chance to get stock and a permanent spot in Billy's corporation. It was somewhat more complicated than that, but that's the gist.

Craig started working, and he loved it. He helped design the shop, got very involved, was away a lot, and I resented it. But it would make Craig self-sufficient, and I couldn't argue with that. I could fume against it, but I couldn't argue.

Of course, I started getting itchy with all that time on my hands. I'd lost my playmate. Carl kept saying he could get me some TV work if I wanted, but I'd never really liked television work.

Without really noticing, I guess I'd retired. I was genuinely surprised when I realized that. I was really out of things by then. My agent had retired and I'd lost all my work contacts, and besides, if I got a job I'd have to give up watching *All My Children*.

I ran into an old chum at one of Estelle's parties. He was a very big man on Broadway and he'd directed a movie or two. He asked me if I'd be interested in reading for a part in a new show he was doing. I almost said, "I don't *read*." Instead, I just said thank you. He sent the script over and, as he said, it was a small part, but very flashy. I checked with my doctor and Craig, and ended up getting the part. Any lingering image of glamour I might have had was about to go down the drain. I had one scene in the second act. I played the lead's father, and my son has asked me over for dinner. My costume was out of some second-hand store—trousers bagged, the crotch was around my ankles, the belt seven inches too big, shirt unpressed. I stooped, I shuffled, I gummed, I acted my age. In the play, my son has asked me over because he feels guilty about neglecting me. My son is between wives, his current affair is a mess, and he can't seem not to make more and more money. I knew my son was trying to buy off his conscience with me and I wouldn't let him. I'd always picked up my marbles, and I'd raised him that way. In the scene I got to be angry and high-minded and feisty and lovable, all in ten minutes. I end up near the door ready to leave, and I say, "You must have been very lonely to have invited me over. I didn't come because I was lonely. All I've gotten for my trouble is a lecture on what a rotten father I was. Well, I haven't been your father for twenty-five years—not since you left us. If you fuck up now, you do it on your own. Don't blame me. I'm too busy for you. I'm busy with what's left. Don't you dare come to my funeral and cry over me. I don't want you there. You're not my son anymore. You're what you've made yourself and I don't like you."

Exit. Applause.

I never left that stage without a big hand. I never took my solo curtain call without getting a rise in applause. I wasn't able to stay with the show too long, but it got me a Tony nomination. I didn't win, but not bad for someone who was seventy. I still knew my craft.

I did the movie, too. It's nice to have that around to look at. I'm proud of it. I got the best reviews I've ever had. Craig prefers my old RKO movies. I look at them and can't remember playing any of the scenes, but I remember all that happened off-camera. I remember the jokes and the horseplay and who was sleeping with whom. There's not a reason in the world to remember any of the lines.

# Afterword

I am hesitant about adding this afterword, because it falls beyond the limits I originally set for this work, which was to explore the long lives of four homosexual friends in their own words. I have tried not to overdirect my narrators or precondition their answers. I have also taken care to exclude myself from their narratives, because to intrude myself seemed something of a violation of the material.

Yet I was a witness to an event that seems necessary of inclusion.

Four months after I finished interviewing my four subjects, Wesley Ober died of the heart attack which had been foreshadowed by several minor coronaries and by frequent unsatisfactory cardiograms. So his friends absorbed the blow of his death through the cushion of preparedness.

It was Robert Regal who, as Ober's executor, was called by the police when the body was found.

Regal quickly arrived at Ober's apartment, checked that his few valuables were in order, and stayed till the doctor confirmed that it was death by heart attack.

Regal called me the next morning to tell me of Ober's death. I felt a great sense of grief and loss.

Ober was cremated and then his friends organized an invitational memorial service at a Fifth Avenue church. Carl Mason called and told me that I would be most welcome at the service. I said that it would please me to attend.

I arrived at the church a few minutes later than I'd planned, after almost everyone was seated. I took a seat near the back of the small chapel that lay to the left of the main altar.

Farther down I could recognize Hicks, Regal, and Mason;

most of the rest of the crowd was expensively dressed and over fifty.

Promptly at eleven, a bell was rung from somewhere up front and the minister appeared, followed by several elderly women, who took seats in the two front pews reserved for them. When the women were settled, the minister moved to the lectern and introduced an eminent theatrical figure who delivered an *ex tempore* eulogy. It was the man who had directed Ober in his last show.

It was all modest, simple, short, and solemn, and I sat there fairly bored, knowing that Wesley Ober would have liked a verbal high kick or two, and even a good laugh. But he was dead and was in no position to do other than take what he got.

Soon we were all standing to sing a hymn I didn't know and which I felt obliged to fake. Not knowing what to do after that, I just sat back down to wait.

I saw the group of women in the two front pews rise and make a sad and stately progress down the aisle, coming my way toward the rear of the church. As they passed me, it suddenly dawned on me that these were Ober's sisters, the five still living, anyway.

They all passed me with downcast eyes, except for one, who I saw examining all the faces as she moved up the aisle. When she glanced at me, she blinked and I had the feeling that her sharp eyes had caught more than my appearance. Something about me had interested her.

Still not knowing what was appropriate, I remained seated till others began filing out. As they came up the aisle I saw many faces that seemed familiar, but I didn't know quite why. Then it dawned on me that many of these people were once very famous, and I knew them through movies I'd seen at revival houses and on late-night TV. I hadn't expected to see them aged and living in New York.

I sat until Billy Hicks drew abreast of me and then I joined him, moving toward the five sisters, who had formed a kind of receiving line just outside the chapel.

The line moved slowly, because everyone was pausing to tell one or another of the sisters how much they had admired or missed or loved Ober. As I waited in the queue with Hicks, I heard the man behind me say in a querulous voice, "I suppose we'll have to pay our respects to the Widow Ober, too." I didn't turn around to see who had spoken.

I mumbled something to one of Ober's sisters and then turned the corner with Hicks into the vestibule of the church.

In the farthest corner I could see that a group of men had collected and that other men moved to the corner, spoke, and then quickly left the church.

When Hicks and I reached the cluster of men I saw a man in his late thirties standing facing us, his back to the stone wall. He looked confused and uncomfortable, and when a man extended his hand to him he took it as if unsure about what to do with it. He held the proferred hand awkwardly and listened to some softly spoken phrase, as if he were trying hard to translate it into some language he knew.

It took me a long moment to realize that I was looking at what the slighting voice had called the "Widow Ober," and what I'd mistaken for disorientation was grief. I realized I was seeing Wesley Ober's lover Craig for the first time.

I felt uneasy. I felt that, through all Ober had told me of Craig, I'd invaded Craig's privacy and he didn't even know who I was. I didn't even know if he knew that I would cover the intimate details of his life with Wes in my book. So, when Hicks went up to say a word to Craig, I held back.

Regal and Hicks, who were standing near Craig, saw me, and motioned me to come over, but I indicated with my head that I would wait nearby till they were free.

I went off a little way and stood near a rack of pamphlets that hung just outside the main doors of the church. I watched the group of men. I saw Billy Hicks lay his hand on Craig's shoulder and leave it there. I saw Hicks's and Regal's concerned attention focused on him.

It seemed awful to me that the man who had given love, caring, and years to Ober should be consigned to the role of a clandestine mourner, a kind of latter-day *Back Street* figure. It was wrong. It was backward. Craig should have been in the front pew, not the sisters who hadn't seen him for years and were here, I felt smugly sure, only for the meager scraps that might fall from his estate.

I felt angry that five women who were surely almost strangers to their brother, who probably were never there to support and love him in life, should now display public sorrow and accept public condolences at his death. It seemed to me the situation was false, wrong, and hurtful to Craig.

I was so deep in my angry reverie that I jumped when she said, "Are you Charles Norman?"

I turned and saw one of Ober's sisters, the one whom I'd interested.

I nodded yes, and she said, "Sorry I startled you. I'm Madeline, Wes's sister. He described you to me. I knew it was you. He told me about you interviewing him for your book. He liked you very much. He didn't say what your book is about. I'm way off in the country, and if you do put Wes in your book I'd love to have a copy. Here's my name and address. I'd appreciate it if you'd write me when the book comes out, so I can get a copy."

I took the slip of paper she held out and told her that I'd be happy to, not knowing if Ober would want his sister to know he was gay, even posthumously.

She started to turn away, and my glance went back to where Craig and some others still stood.

I didn't notice her stop or see her follow my glance, so I was startled again by her when she asked, "Do you know if that's Craig?"

I said, "I think so. Yes, I'm sure it must be."

She said, "I wish I could tell him how sorry I am for him, but I don't know him. He might be embarrassed."

She had said that as if she were thinking aloud.

Then she said, "I don't know whether I'm speaking out of turn or not, but Wes didn't have any secrets from me, even the ones he didn't tell me. But it's too late to worry about any of that, isn't it? If you talk to Craig, tell him that I'm very sorry. I'm sorry for his loss. Wes was a loving man and he had good sense.

"Well, good luck with your book. I wish we had time to talk, but I'm going home tonight."

She moved away to rejoin her sisters, who were waiting at the side exit, and they left together.

I now think that when I began this book, I hoped that I would freeze four lives and their times in amber, that I would end up with facts that, given enough time and study, would yield absolute truths. But when I saw Billy, Robert, and Carl that day in church, I knew that whatever this book managed to do, it would not resolve into the certainties I'd hoped for.

In a way, I would like to track the surviving three men to their memorial services. I would like a neat book, a book with a neat ending in which all the lives covered are fully resolved.

I may have come close to accomplishing what I set out to do, but I must admit that I feel I still stand short of my goal. I can't help but feel that even a hundred voices wouldn't be a sufficient chorus to tell the story I had in mind, that what really happens to any people, gay or straight, must remain as shadowed as the lives of these men I have tried so hard to reveal in full light.

# GAY PAPERBOUND

Avon publishes more than three dozen titles of homosexual interests, ranging from popular fiction to works of scholarly concern. Here are a selection of the most recent titles:

**A HISTORY OF SHADOWS**
**Robert C. Reinhart**
79616/$2.95
Avon Original

A wonderfully evocative novel that follows the life and times of four fascinating gay men, all friends for years, from their coming-of-age in the 1930's to their maturity in the 1970's. Together they share the pains—and joys—of being homosexual during an era when they were condemned and ostracized.

**THE LONG SHOT**
**Paul Monette**
76828/$5.95
Avon Original

In this witty and dramatic novel, Paul Monette reveals a side of Hollywood rarely shown on this side of the camera. The apparent double suicide of Jasper Cokes and Harry Dawes on the night of the Academy Awards brings together a remarkable group of characters and involves them in a mystery of the flesh and spirit.

**GAYWYCK**
**Vincent Virga**
75820/$2.95
Avon Original

Set in an extravagant Gramercy Park townhouse and a sumptuous Long Island mansion at the turn of the century, GAYWYCK is the first gay Gothic ever published.

**VERMILION**
**Nathan Aldyne**
76596/$2.25
Avon Original

The unlikeliest detective duo to ever hit the streets of Boston—a gay bartender and his real estate agent sidekick—investigate the bizarre death of a young male hustler and in the process discover some very kinky games being played in town.

**THE GOLD DIGGERS**
**Paul Monette**
43026/$4.95
Avon Original

...lizing mystery, a comedy of manners, a potent love
...biting commentary on homosexual lifestyles
...tyles in general.